Biology 151 Laboratory Manual

Investigations into Living Systems

Department of Biology, Winthrop University

Phillip Shelp

Australia • Brazil • Japan • Korea • Mexico • Singapore • Spain • United Kingdom • United States

Biology 151 Laboratory Manual: Investigations into Living Systems

Phillip Shelp

Executive Editor:
Michael Stranz

Managing Lab Editor:
Jeff Nunn

Custom Lab Editors:
Cooper Gouge, John Horvath

Custom Production Editor:
Jennifer Flinchpaugh

Project Coordinators:
Lisa Donahue, Peg Hagar

Senior Pre-Press Specialist:
Riley Gibb

Production Supervisor-Labs:
Melanie Evans

Rights and Permissions Specialist:
Kalina Ingham Hintz

Senior Marketing Coordinator:
Sara Mercurio

Cover Image:
Getty Images

ISBN-13: 978-0-495-48336-6

ISBN-10: 0-495-48336-2

Cengage Learning
5191 Natorp Boulevard
Mason, OH 45040
USA

Printed in the United States of America

Custom Contents

1 SCIENTIFIC METHOD

Objectives

After completing this unit you will be able to:

- identify the steps of the scientific method
- compare personal problem solving techniques to the scientific method
- design experiments, collect data and test a hypothesis

Introduction

In this unit you will develop the skills to conduct and critique scientific investigations. Throughout this laboratory course you will be investigating biology by asking questions, proposing explanations, designing experiments, predicting results, collecting and analyzing data, and interpreting your results. This process is called the **scientific method**. Scientists may not always follow these guidelines exactly, but some form of the process guides their work. The scientific method has the following steps:

1. Observe natural phenomena.
2. Construct a hypothesis to explain the observation.
3. Test the hypothesis with experiments.
4. Draw conclusions about the hypothesis based on the data resulting from experimentation.

The **hypothesis** is your proposed explanation of phenomena you have been studying. A workable hypothesis must be logical, based on sound observation, and most importantly, testable.

I. Scientific Method

Scientific inquiry is an approach to problem solving that may utilize all of a person's senses and ability to reason. Additional tools, such as microscopes, balances, and chemical tests, can be used to aid in investigations.

There are two methods people use to solve problems. One approach is **inductive reasoning**, which involves making a conclusion based on observations. Using this process, pieces of information are used to form a generalization. We make an inductive leap when we go from observed examples to formulating a general principle that will hold true for all examples.

The other approach to problem solving is **deductive reasoning**, which involves drawing specific conclusions from general principles. This process uses generalizations to predict new relationships.

EXERCISE 3.1 What's in the box?

Work in small groups of two or three.

1. Obtain a numbered, sealed box from the lab table and record the number of the box (*Table 3.1*). Determine what is in the box using your senses, a metric balance, and a magnet. Gather data about the unknown object and record the data (*Table 3.1*).

	Test	Data
1		
2		
3		
4		
5		

Table 3.1 Tests and data for unknown

Note: An empty box identical to the one containing the unknown object is provided for comparison. Subtract the weight of the empty box from the weight of the box with the unknown to determine the weight of the unknown.

2. Using inductive reasoning, create a hypothesis about the unknown object in your box. Describe the unknown object with words and a drawing.

3. Go to the lab table containing objects identical to what might be in your box (*Figure 3.1*). Using deductive reasoning, select the object that best matches your hypothesis and test the item to see if it matches your hypothesis. List your tests and record the data (*Table 3.2*).

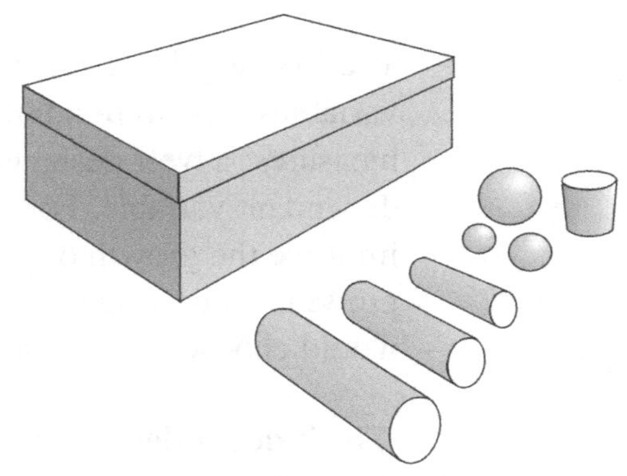

Figure 3.1 Possible contents in the box

	Test	**Data**
1		
2		
3		
4		
5		
Name of Unknown		

Table 3.2 Tests and data to confirm hypothesis

4. Do the observations you recorded in *Table 3.2* support the hypothesis you created from data in *Table 3.1*? If not, test another object.

II. Designing an Experiment

A hypothesis is tested by doing a controlled experiment. An experiment is designed to produce results proving or disproving the hypothesis. Well-designed experiments have an **experimental group** and a **control group**. In the experimental group, one factor is altered in some manner. In the control group, the test is performed under the same conditions as in the experimental group except no change is made to the independent variable.

The first step in designing an experiment is to identify all the variables. The **dependent variable** is what the investigator measures; a well-designed experiment will have an effect on the dependant variable. For example, if you want to determine ways to improve the growth of your houseplants, you could measure plant growth, water usage, or flower production of the plants. You would choose one of these plant traits as your dependent variable.

The **independent variable** is the variable the investigator varies during the experiment in hopes of affecting the dependent variable. The amount of fertilizer, light, and water are all examples of independent variables that would affect how well your plants grow.

All variables other than the independent variable being tested must be held constant. The variables held constant are called **controlled variables**. If you have chosen fertilizer as your independent variable in testing house plant growth, you must make sure to test the plants under identical conditions of light, moisture, and soil type so these variables will not influence the independent variable.

- Why is it important to test one independent variable at a time?

Another important part of a well designed experiment is replication. A scientist must be able to repeat the experiment numerous times using exactly the same conditions to see if the results are consistent.

EXERCISE 3.2 Designing an experiment to test the effectiveness of disinfectants

Microorganisms such as bacteria and fungi are a normal part of our environment. They are found in the air, soil, water, and on our bodies. We have co-evolved with these microbes and most of them do no harm. You don't see microorganisms around you because they are so small. However, if the bacteria or fungi floating in the air land on a rich source of nutrients, they will grow rapidly and produce a colony of cells that can be seen with the unaided eye. Bacteria form smooth, shiny colonies. Molds form thick, fleshy colonies that are larger than bacteria colonies. Yeast colonies grow slower than molds and sometimes have a yellow color.

Microorganisms can be grown in petri plates which contain a sterile nutrient media called agar.

1. Examine the culture plate provided, and identify the microorganisms growing on the agar as bacteria, mold, or yeast colonies. Draw and label the cultures (*Figure 3.2*).

Figure 3.2 Culture plate with microorganisms

The disinfectant solutions sold in grocery stores may or may not be effective at killing microorganisms. Your job in this exercise is to test the effectiveness of several disinfectants and form a conclusion as to which prevents microorganism growth most effectively.

2. With your group, observe the different disinfectants provided in the laboratory.

Disinfectant	Active ingredient
1.	
2.	
3.	
4.	
5.	
6.	

Table 3.3 Disinfectants

3. Form a testable hypothesis with your group. Share this with the instructor and decide which hypothesis the class will test.

   Group Hypothesis:

   Test Hypothesis:

4. Distribute the disinfectants to be tested among the student groups.

5. Obtain four sterile petri plates containing agar media. Label two "control" and two with the disinfectant you are testing. Also put the date and your group name on the bottom of the plates.

6. Test the effectiveness of your disinfectant on different surfaces in the lab such as table tops, books, etc. Use two sterile cotton swabs to pick up microorganisms on your test surface. Run each swab once across the surface, in different areas. On a second control plate, run each swab across the surface as on the first plate.

7. Use your disinfectant as recommended by the manufacturer for normal household use, and clean your test surface. When

dry, run two more sterile swabs across the surface and wipe each swab on a different test plate.

8. Incubate the plates at 40°C for best microbe growth.

Note: You will examine your plates during the next scheduled lab period and collect and analyze your data then.

9. Observe your plates. Count the colonies on your two control and two test plates, and record the data (*Table 3.4*).

Disinfectant ________________

	Control		Disinfectant	
	Plate #1	Plate #2	Plate #1	Plate #2
Bacteria				
Mold				
Yeast				
Total Colonies				

Table 3.4 Number of microorganism colonies on petri plates

10. Compile the class data and record each groups results (*Table 3.5*).

Type of Disinfectant	Total # Colonies Disinfectant	Total # Colonies Control

Table 3.5 Effect of different disinfectants on microbe growth

- What conclusions can you draw from your data?

- What was the control used in this experiment and why was it used?

- Was your original hypothesis correct?

- What changes would you make to improve this experiment?

EXERCISE 3.3 Design an experiment to measure cardiovascular fitness

Cardiovascular fitness can be determined by measuring a person's pulse rate before and after aerobic exercise. A person who is physically fit may have a slower starting pulse rate. After exercise, and his or her pulse rate should return to normal sooner. Other factors, such as age, body size, gender, and whether a person smokes or not, will have an effect on pulse rate.

1. In small groups, discuss several specific questions about an independent variable related to cardiovascular fitness. List your questions below.

   Question: a.

   b.

   c.

   d.

2. Select one question and propose a testable hypothesis.

   Hypothesis:

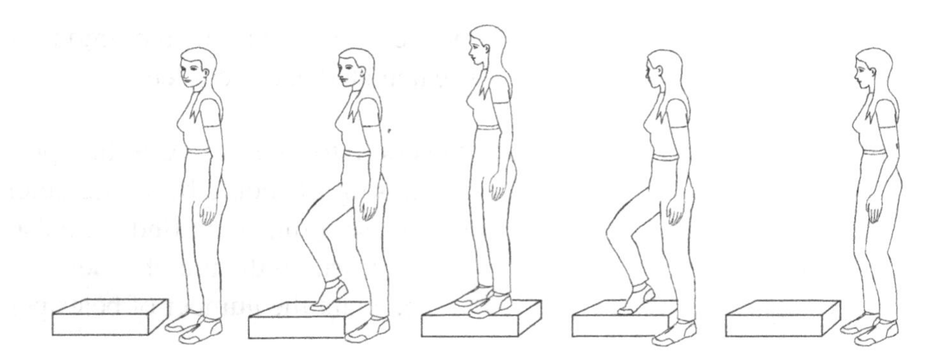

Figure 3.3 Step test

A test to measure cardiovascular fitness called the **step test** is shown in *Figure 3.3*. The subject steps up and down on an eight inch platform for three minutes at a rate of 24 steps per minute. A metronome is used to ensure a constant step rate. The subject should step up and then step down again.

3. Record the parts of the experiment below:

   Dependent variable

   Independent variable

   Controlled variables

   Control

   Testing procedure

4. Working in groups, choose two students to test your hypothesis using the step test. The other group members will measure pulse rate and calculate recovery times for the test subjects.

   Note: Students with respiratory or circulatory disorders should not be test subjects.

   The test subject's pulse rate is measured before the test (initial pulse rate), after three minutes of stepping (3 minute pulse rate), and at one minute intervals after the test. The subject's recovery time, the time required to return to normal pulse rate, is calculated and recorded.

5. Procedure for measuring resting pulse rate:
   a. subject should be sitting quietly;
   b. use 3 fingers to find the pulse in the radial artery in the wrist, on the thumb side;
   c. count the number of beats per minute.

6. Record your results from the step test in *Table 3.6* and then on the class data sheet.

	Test Subject 1	**Test Subject 2**
Initial Pulse Rate (beats/min)		
3 Minute Pulse Rate (beats/min)		
Pulse Recovery Time (min)		

Table 3.6 Pulse rates in test subjects

7. Record the data gathered by the class (*Table 3.7*).

Test Subject 1: Condition ______________________

	1	2	3	4	5	6	Avg.
Initial Pulse Rate							
3 Minute Pulse Rate							
Pulse Recovery Time							

Test Subject 2: Condition ______________________

	1	2	3	4	5	6	Avg.
Initial Pulse Rate							
3 Minute Pulse Rate							
Pulse Recovery Time							

Table 3.7 Pulse rates in multiple test subjects

- What conclusions can you draw from this experiment?

- Write a summary statement for your experiments. Use data to support or reject your hypothesis.

- How could the experiment be improved?

Summary Questions

____________________ 1. What the investigator measures; it is affected by the experiment.

____________________ 2. Variables that are held constant during an experiment.

____________________ 3. What the investigator varies in the experiment.

____________________ 4. Tentative explanation for an observation.

____________________ 5. Drawing specific conclusions from general principles.

6. Identify the dependent and independent variables in the following examples. Underline the dependent variable and circle the independent variable.

   Rats are fed french fries or corn for two weeks. Percent weight gain is measured.

   Different types of wood are burned and heat production is measured.

   Late model cars are driven and fuel efficiency in miles per gallon is measured.

   Children in day-care centers may or may not be required to wash their hands when they arrive at school. Incidence of cold or flu is recorded.

7. Suggest a controlled variable for each example above.

2 MEASUREMENT (by James Johnston, PhD.)

Objectives

After completing this unit you will be able to:

- Understand which units of measure to use in determining length, volume, weight and temperature
- Use an electronic balance to determine an object's weight and a Vernier Caliper to determine an object's length

Introduction

Learning the philosophy and activities of science is like learning a new language. In fact, it is a new language to some degree. As with language, the only way to learn is to practice so the elements of the discipline become familiar. One area where science differs from your everyday experiences is in the units of measure we use. Science uses the metric system. The entire system (except for time units) is based on multiples of 10 (especially 100 and 1000). In this course we will use the following units.

TO MEASURE	USE THESE UNITS
Time	seconds (S), minutes (M), hours (H)
Length	millimeters (mm), centimeters (cm), meters (m), kilometers (km) 10 mm = 1 cm; 1000 mm = 1 m; 100 cm= 1 m; 1000 m= 1 km
Volume	milliliters (1 ml = 1 cubic centimeter or 1 cc); liters (l) 1000 ml (or cc) = 1 liter (l)
Weight	grams (g); kilograms (kg) 1000g=1kg
Temperature	degrees Celsius (oC). This is sometimes called "centigrade" but Celsius is preferred. We do not use Fahrenheit.

Note that the prefixes milli-, centi-, and kilo-are clues to what the relationship is:
Milli -= 1000ths; a meter has 1000 mm; a liter has 1000 ml. Thus you are looking at small pieces or parts of a larger thing, as many as a 1000 of them.
Centi-= 100ths; a meter has 100 cm; a liter has 100 cl (but note that volume is rarely measured in centiliters – use milliliters or liters). You are looking at as many as 100 small pieces of a larger thing.
Kilo-= groups of 1000; 1000 g in a kilogram; 20 kg contain 20,000 g.

When do you use a particular unit? It becomes a matter of experience or common sense, just as when you know to measure something in inches rather than furlongs or light-years.

Time is not a problem, you're used to this already.

What about length? Try this for a guide: if you'd measure something in fractions of an inch use millimeters; if you'd measure it in inches, use centimeters; it it's something you'd measure in yards, use meters. If it's something you'd measure in miles, use kilometers.

For volume try this: if you'd measure it in anything less than a quart use ml (or cc, remember they are the same), otherwise use liters.

For weight try this: if it's less than 2 pounds, use grams; otherwise use kilograms.

For temperature just report the reading on the thermometer in degrees Celsius (oC).

How do you convert from one metric unit to another?

It is very simple, just move the decimal point. For example, let us assume that a paper clip weighs 1,200 milligrams. How many grams is this? Since you know that the prefix milli- means 1000^{ths} (0.001) you would move the decimal point three places to the left to convert from milligrams to grams (1,200 mg = 1.2 g). You can remember that if you are moving to a larger unit move the decimal to the left (remember larger moves left).

If you were converting from a larger unit to a smaller unit (e.g. from grams to milligrams) you move the decimal to the right. We have not come up with a good phrase to remember this one; perhaps you can and share it with rest of us.

Use the chart below to practice converting between different metric units.
Metric Measurements

Decimal	Exponent	Length	Mass	Volume
1000	10^3	Kilometer (km)	Kilogram (kg)	Kiloliter (kL)
100	10^2			
10	10^1			
1	10^0	Meter (m)	Gram (g)	Liter (L)
0.1	10^{-1}			Deciliter (dL)
0.01	10^{-2}	Centimeter (cm)		
0.001	10^{-3}	Millimeter (mm)	Milligram (mg)	Milliliter (mL)
0.0001	10^{-4}			
0.00001	10^{-5}			
0.000001	10^{-6}	Micrometer (um)	Microgram (ug)	Microliter (uL)

You'll have to practice with these units to get used to them. Use money or other common place items for practice. Here are some things to do to familiarize your self with these systems:

1. How thick is a penny?_____________
2. How much does a penny weigh? ____________
3. What is the room's temperature? ______________
4. How long is your index finger? ____________
5. How long is your foot? ___________
6. How long is the lab room? _____________
7. How many milliliters are there in 10 beans (how are you going to figure that one out?)? [Hint: 1 ml = 1 cubic centimeter] _________________
8. How many milliliters are there in a plastic flower pot (again, how are you going to figure that one out?)? _________________

Measuring Devices: What do you use to measure this stuff? Here's a list:

To Measure	Use
Time	watch w/second hand, digital watch, stopwatch
Length	millimeter ruler, centimeter ruler, calipers, meter stick, metric tape measure
Volume	For rough measures use a beaker or flask. For more exact measurement, use a graduate cylinder. As is true of beakers and flasks, these come in different sizes. Use the appropriate size.
Temperature	thermometer
Weight	Use a balance. Directions for the use of an electronic balance follow. One word of caution, never put stuff to be weighed directly on the balance pan; always use a weighing cup or piece of paper.

Electronic balance:

A) Put the weighing cup or piece of paper on the balance pan.
B) Turn on the machine and press "TARE" (If the machine is already on, put the weighing cup on and immediately press "TARE".) The display will give a readout of "—" and then reset itself to 0. Taring means that the balance automatically takes into account the weight of the weighing cup for all subsequent weighings.
C) CAREFULLY measure out the material to be weighed. Don't drop stuff from a great height; this is a delicate instrument.
D) Read the weight on the display. If the weight bounces between two readings, the material weighs in the middle of the two numbers shown.

Vernier Calipers: These measuring devices are good for measuring small distances or for measuring down to tenths or hundredths of mm. The calipers consist of two parts, a body and a sliding piece. The calipers we use have inches along the top of the body and mm along the bottom of the body. WE WILL ONLY USE THE MM, of course, so pay attention only to the mm scale on the bottom of the body.

The calipers have two beak-like regions. The one on the top is for measuring the inside diameter of something (like the mouth of a jar or the inside of a piece of tubing) and the lower one is for measuring the outside diameter or thickness or something.

Slide the bar along the body, just to see how it works. Now, let's measure the diameter of a nickel. Put a nickel in the space formed between the sliding bar and the body so that one of the beak pieces is on each edge of the nickel (Why are we using this beak instead of the other one?) Make sure you close the calipers so that the nickel is held tightly.

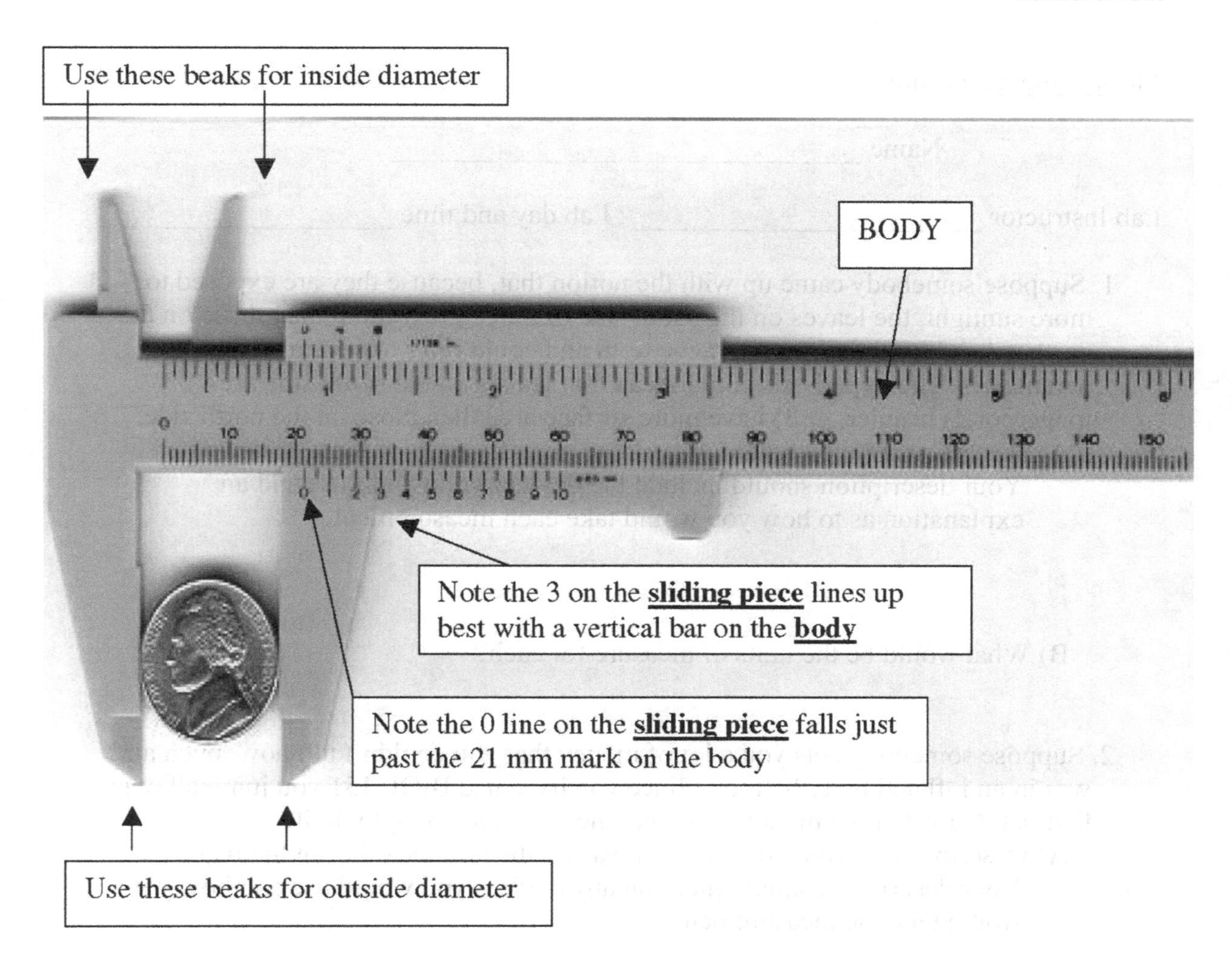

Look at the lower scale on the body. You will notice that it goes from 0 mm to 155 mm. Below this scale you will see on the sliding portion of the calipers another scale that goes from 0 to 10; this scale measures in tenths and five-hundredths of a mm.

The scale on the body, the one that measures whole mm, is where to look first. To find out approximately how wide the nickel is, look at the point where the 0 on the sliding scale lines up with the scale on the body. In this case it looks to be a little past 21 mm. So we know that a nickel is between 21 and 22 mm in diameter. We can get more precise than that.

To get the fractional part of the measurement look on the sliding piece scale and use your eye to estimate which one of the vertical bars lines up best with a vertical bar on the body. In this instance, it looks like the 3 on the sliding scale lines up best with a vertical bar on the body, so the nickel has a diameter of around 21.3 mm.

Use the calipers to measure the thickness (not the width) of the nickel. How thick is the nickel?

Measurement Questions

Name ______________________________

Lab Instructor ______________________ ; Lab day and time __________________

1. Suppose somebody came up with the notion that, because they are exposed to more sunlight, the leaves on the south side of a tree grow more than those on the north side. Growth is a pretty vague term and could refer to several different parameters. The hypothesis could mean that leaves on the south side are 1) longer, or 2) heavier, or 3) have more surface area than those on the north side.
   A) Describe what you would measure to quantify each of these 3 parameters. Your description should include the devices you would use and an explanation as to how you would take each measurement.

   B) What would be the units of measure for each?

2. Suppose somebody bets you a lot of money that you couldn't tell how much air was in an inflated party balloon. Since you have had BIOL 151 you jump all over that bet. Now that the money is on the line, how are going to do it?
   A) Describe what you would do to measure the volume of air in the balloon. Your description should mention any devices you would use and how you would take the measurements.

   B) What units of measure will result?

3. Your Uncle Fred tells you that an object floats if it is less dense than water. He goes on to tell you that an object's density is its weight divided by its volume. How would you calculate the density of a wine bottle cork?
   A) Describe what you would do to find the density of the cork. Your description should mention the devices you would use and how you would use them.

   B) What units of measure will result and what would be the final unit of measure for density?

3 STATISTICS (By William Rogers, Ph.D.)

Objectives

After completing this unit you will be able to:

- Understand how to ask and analyze scientific questions
- Recognize variables and the types of data they represent
- Know which statistical test is appropriate for a particular scientific problem and what the test's results mean.

Introduction

There once was a rancher who had two horses and he wanted to make sure he and his ranch hands could tell them apart. So, one day he measured each horse every way he could. After looking at the numbers he got, he realized that there was indeed a difference. The black horse was about ¼ inch taller than the white one.

You may feel that the above story shows how statistics are a waste of your time and that you can tell when two or more things are not the same. Actually, it is rarely the case that differences are so obvious. Objects in the real world can differ in subtle ways and we need an objective way to tell them apart. Statistical analysis takes subjective judgment out of the process and gives the observer a non-biased technique for deciding if sets of things are the same or different. Statistical testing of data in science is absolutely essential.

What Do We Need to Understand in Order to Do Statistical Analysis?

QUESTIONS:

The ability to ask questions intelligently and clearly is central to scientific inquiry. Asking questions is a natural human behavior and it is done really well by kids. Children are naturally curious - they want to know and understand their surroundings. However, as some people get older and allegedly more "sophisticated" they feel it is wrong or silly to ask questions. We, as scientists, feel otherwise and for us it is essential that we ask dozens or more as we go through the day. It saddens teachers when a student prefaces a question with "I know this is a stupid question but…" So, get in the habit of asking questions.

Questions in science begin in the same way as they do in any endeavor. They start with such words as "what", "how", "when", "how often", "what if…", etc. A scientist doesn't stop there, though. The question is only the beginning of the process. In fact, the next step ought to be a little voice inside your head that says, in response to the question just posed, "I don't know, but I'll try to find out."

When we ask a question in science we need to make sure we fully understand it. If we do, then what follows is much easier. Our question usually asks about the effect of one or more influences on some phenomenon of interest to us. For example, if we wanted to know whether male babies weigh the same as female babies at birth, we are asking something that could be phrased, "What is the effect of sex on birth weights in humans?" Notice how we can take the original vaguely stated "Is there a difference…" question and turn it into something where we can see two things: a) The phenomenon of interest to us - here it's possible differences in birth weight; and b) The particular feature of that system whose effect we are investigating – in this case, it's the sex of the baby. In fact, if you can state your question in the pattern, "What is the influence of _________ on __________?" you are well on your way to understanding not only statistics but the scientific process in general.

POSSIBLE ANSWERS TO YOUR QUESTION:

In science, we don't just ask questions, we propose answers to our questions. These possible answers are educated guesses called "hypotheses" (singular = "hypothesis"). These are tentative answers to our question. "Tentative" means that we recognize we might be wrong.

The particular answer you think is the likely one is called your "working hypothesis". It is what is likely to be the answer to your question based on information you already know. For instance, you might think that, since adult males are generally larger than adult females, male babies are likely to be larger than female babies. On the other hand, you might argue that since a baby has to get through the birth canal, babies, regardless of their sex, should be about the same size.

How do you decide if you are right or wrong? You test your hypothesis. Testing the hypothesis is the job of an experiment and your experiment will either support or reject your hypothesis.

We have to recognize that, even in the simple system we are investigating, there are always several possible outcomes. In the present question there are three possibilities:

a) There is no difference between male and female birth weights.
b) Males are heavier at birth.
c) Females are heavier at birth.

The first one is called the "null hypothesis" and it is ALWAYS one of the possible outcomes. The null hypothesis is the one that says there is no difference between the groups being compared. The other two are "alternative hypotheses"; note that they are just different ways to say that the groups ARE different. There is always at least one alternative hypothesis.

VARIABLES:

Something you have to realize and put into your world-view is that no two things in the universe are really absolutely identical. EVERYTHING has influences acting on it that cause small, subtle differences between it and supposedly identical objects. This is true for coins from the same mint in a given year, the breakdown records for automobiles from different plants of a given car manufacturer, and even supposedly "identical" twins. (As an example of the last case, there is a pair of brothers, Jose and Ozzie Canseco – they are identical twins and few people can tell them apart easily. Both play baseball but while Jose was a star in the Major Leagues, his supposedly identical twin, Ozzie, never made it out of minor leagues. So much for being "identical".) In short, the message is that everything varies and from that idea we get the term "variable".

In the question just asked, what can vary? That is, what can differ between individual items (babies) in the system under study? There are two things: a) sex of the child and b) birth weight. From the question asked, those are, in fact, the only variables. If your question also concerned age of the mother or place of birth (home versus hospital, for example) those would also be variables but since they were not part of the question, they are not relevant variables at this point. Do you begin to see why clearly asking the question is so important? It lets us clearly state what are the relevant variables and this is critical to statistical analysis.

Now, while both sex of the child and a child's birth weight are variables, they are different types of variables. (See, even variables vary.) One is an independent variable and the other is a dependent variable. How do you know which is which? It's easy if you asked the question properly. Remember the little model, "What is the influence of __________ on _____________?" The independent variable goes in the first blank and the dependent variable goes in the second one. *The independent variable* is the one whose influence you will measure by looking at how it *affects the values of the dependent variable*. (Remember that if there is more than one independent variable they will all be listed before the word "on" in the model. Thus, you could ask the complicated question, "What are the effects of sex of child, mother's age and location of birth ON birth weight?" but that's a complicated thing to analyze. Let's just stick with a single independent variable for now.)

To be a variable something has to exist in at least two different states of being. That is, a variable is a category of things that occur in at least two different forms. Our independent variable is SEX. Note that "male" and "female" are NOT variables. They are forms or, in statistical jargon, LEVELS, of the variable sex. Sex comes in two forms; the forms or levels are either male or female. Moreover, every independent variable must have at least two levels of that variable. If there are not at least two levels, it isn't a variable.

Our dependent variable is what we actually measure over the course of the experiment – this is where we get our experimental data. It's called the dependent variable because its value potentially depends on the influence of the independent variable. Here, our dependent variable is birth weight. Obviously, it's a variable. We know that babies vary in how much they weigh at birth. Each weight can be thought of as a level of the dependent variable, birth weight.

Below, state some potential independent variables and give the levels of the variable for each. Do not use sex as one of them.

	Independent Variable	Levels
1		
2		
3		
4		
5		
6		
7		
8		

Now, list at least one potential dependent variable that could be associated with each of the independent variables you listed above.

	Independent Variable	Dependent Variable
1		
2		
3		
4		
5		
6		
7		
8		

DATA AND DATA TYPES:

We have stated our question so that we can identify our variables. We know in our example that we are interested in the influence of a baby's sex on its weight at birth. In addition to representing different types of variables, these things also happen to illustrate different types of data.

Data can be divided into two types: a) discrete or b) continuous. These are mutually exclusive categories. Let's get a look at each one.

Discrete Data Types – When you can sort things by their characteristics or attributes, you are dealing with discrete data types or "discrete variables". Such things are counted and cannot have fractional values. Use, as your model, the idea of sorting things into piles or into bins. How might you sort some items? They'd go either into that pile or into that pile or into that pile, etc. What are examples of characteristics or attributes? How about color? An item will be either blue or yellow or red. It cannot be blue-and-a-half, red-and-a-third, yellow.6932, etc. In our question, our independent variable is an example of a discrete data type. The child is either going to be male or it is going to be female.

List here another 8 categories (other than color and sex) that real world items can fall into if they represent discrete data types:

1

2

3

4

5

6

7

8

Continuous Data Types – Continuous data types or "continuous variables", CAN logically have fractional values. They are things that are measured using rulers, scales, speedometers, etc. They have units of measurement associated with them – things like kilometers, liters, hours/minutes/seconds, temperature, etc. They cannot logically be sorted into non-overlapping categories because they can theoretically have any intermediate value between points along a line. Thus, a table could be measured in centimeters. With casual precision, you might say, "It's about 250 centimeters long." However, someone doing more careful measurements might find that it is 250.9 centimeters and another person with better equipment might discover that it is actually 250.8768 centimeters.

Another thing to keep in mind is that when you divide one data type by another you automatically get a continuous variable. As an example, note that both peanuts and elephants are discrete items – they can be counted. However, if you want to ask a question whose answer would come out in number of peanuts PER elephant (peanuts/elephant) then that would give you continuous data because you are dividing number of peanuts by number of elephants and that CAN have a fractional value.

In our birth weight question, the weights of the babies will obviously give us continuous data. We know this for at least two reasons. First, weight has units associated with it (pounds and ounces or kilograms and grams). That alone should tell you. Second, you are not shocked when something's weight is reported as a fractional value. We feel comfortable with a report of a weight of 6 pounds, 7 ounces (which is equal to 6.4375 pounds – do you know why?)

Now, list below 8 other examples of continuous data types other than the ones given to you above. Make sure the last 3 are formed from division of various data types.

1

2

3

4

5

6

7

8

STILL, WHAT'S THE POINT OF STATISTICS?

Good, you're asking questions. Keep it up. Let's start on the answer, using our baby weight question.

Remember, in order to answer your question you need to do an experiment. In this case, the experiment can be quite simple. For example, if you got the records for all the babies born in a particular hospital for a given year, you might have hundreds of weights. The first thing you would do is to divide the weights into the two discrete categories, male and female, the levels of the independent variable "sex". (At least I HOPE that's what you'd do.) In each category you'd have a bunch of weights (the dependent variable) and these weights would range quite widely, especially if you included premature babies.

Actually, for simplicity's sake, let's take a smaller sample, say the birth weights of your classmates. Here's a hypothetical set of findings:

Birth Weights for a Hypothetical Class of Non-Biology Majors at Winthrop University.
(Weights are reported in kilograms.)

MALES	FEMALES
2.44	1.93
2.50	2.19
2.53	2.19
2.76	2.39
2.84	2.47
2.90	2.53
2.93	2.53
2.93	2.78
3.72	2.84
4.20	3.72
4.80	4.55
	4.67
	4.80

Now, remember, these numbers represent the DEPENDENT variable and they are CONTINUOUS data. What we want to know is whether, ON AVERAGE, one sex or the other is larger at birth.

Notice that above I wrote that we were concerned with the AVERAGE baby of each sex. You may feel that we are changing the rules since we didn't put the word "average" in the question. However, it will be there from now on – it's implicit because of the idea of variation. Things vary but when we ask whether two or more groups of objects differ, we want to know if ON AVERAGE they do so. There will always be unusually large or strong or small or unusually whatever members of data sets. We just accept that. What we want to know is what is typical.

You might have come into this question feeling you know the answer. You may even want one sex to be larger at birth. The point of statistics is to answer the question while at the same time keeping your biases out of getting the answer. It doesn't matter what you think or what you want. If the data have been gathered honestly, they will answer the question when we apply a statistical test to them.

So, just look at the lists of numbers. Can you tell what the answer to our question is just by looking? You might think you can. After all, aren't four of the females smaller than the smallest male? On the other hand, aren't two of the largest females larger than all but one male and aren't the largest values for both sexes identical? It should be clear that we need to do more than just look at the numbers. It's time to turn to – GASP – math.

Before we go on, notice that we have to deal with more than just a few numbers. We need to have a large sample of each sex in order to catch the variation inherent in the system. Actually, our sample of 11 males and 13 females is not all that large but it will have to do for now; a really large sample would be in the hundreds or thousands. Whatever the number of data points, we refer to it as our "SAMPLE SIZE". Here our sample size is 11 males and 13 females.

So, how do we estimate what is typical for each sex? We use the average or MEAN. We add all the weights (the dependent variable) for each sex and divide by the number of individuals of that sex. (In reality, we use a calculator that does all that for us.) For males, the mean is 3.14 kilograms; for females, the mean is 3.05 kilograms. Going back to your first grade math, you would look at the number for the males, compare it with the one for the females and you would declare the males to be larger on average. And you would probably be wrong.

Huh? Isn't 3.14 larger than 3.05? Yes, it is a larger number but it does not necessarily represent an actual *statistically significant* difference. Each mean has several numbers (= data points) that have contributed to it: eleven for the males and thirteen for the females. To answer our question we have to pay attention to the way the data points are spread out. If they are narrowly spread and there is little or no overlap between the two sexes then each mean will probably represent a really different average birth weight. However, if they are both widely spread, or if one is narrowly spread and the other is wide so that in either case they overlap, then the means probably do not represent real, *significant* differences.

How do we find this spread of the data points? It's represented by a thing called the VARIANCE (or by the square root of the variance, the STANDARD DEVIATION.) Both of these are measures of how much variability there is around each mean. They are essential for figuring out the answer to our question. They are not easy to calculate but fortunately, there are now inexpensive calculators that do this for you automatically when you use the device's statistical mode to figure out the mean.

So, lets make another table to see what we know so far. It will include the mean, the variance, the standard deviation and the number of data points we have for each level of the variable. These things are all called "Summary Statistics". They help paint a picture for us and they are essential for the next step.

<u>Summary Statistics for a Sample of Birth Weights for Male and Female Humans</u>

	MALES	FEMALES
Mean (= $\bar{X}$)	3.14	3.05
Variance (= Var)	0.587	1.045
[Standard Dev.	0.766	1.023]
Sample Size (= n)	11	13

Okay, big, fat, hairy deal. Now what? Now we turn to a technique or a set of rules called a STATISTICAL TEST. In this case, we use one called the t-Test. The rules that led us to use the t-Test are:

a) The dependent variable (baby weight) is measured with continuous data.

b) We are looking to see if there is a difference between two means (one for each level of the variable "sex").

What does this test look like? It's a series of steps in a very convenient package - a formula. Just follow the steps in the formula and you'll come out with a number. That number, called "t-CALCULATED" will take us to our answer. Here's the formula:

$$t_{(calculated)} = \frac{\left| \overline{X}_1 - \overline{X}_2 \right|}{\sqrt{\dfrac{[(n_1 - 1)(Var_1)] + [(n_2 - 1)(Var_2)]}{n_1 + n_2 - 2}} \sqrt{\dfrac{1}{n_1} + \dfrac{1}{n_2}}}$$

So, just plug in the numbers you got above:

$$t_{(calculated)} = \frac{\left| 3.14 - 3.05 \right|}{\sqrt{\dfrac{[(11-1)(0.587)] + [(13-1)(1.05)]}{11 + 13 - 2}} \sqrt{\dfrac{1}{11} + \dfrac{1}{13}}}$$

$t_{(calculated)} = 0.23976 = 0.240$

(Your lab instructor will also help walk you through this thing.)

When you get a value for $t_{calculated}$, what does that tell you? Again, there's a very simple process that you follow. First, you need to figure our your "degrees of freedom". Degrees of freedom (= "d.f."), for our purposes, is an index to help you look up something in a table. How do you figure out the d.f.? It's different for every test but for the t-Test, you take the sample size for each level of the variable (here, it's 11 for males and 13 for females) add them together and subtract 2. So, d.f. in this instance is [(11 + 13) – 2] = [24 – 2] = 22.

Now, you go to Table 1 (page 21), look up 22 degrees of freedom in the chart and you find a number associated with it. This is called the “Critical Value”. In this instance, the critical value for d.f. = 22 is 2. 074. Here is a rule that finally lets you decide what your data have told you:

If your calculated value is greater than or equal to the critical value, then you REJECT your null hypothesis. (Remember, your null hypothesis is that there is no significant difference between the two means.) In other words, if you reject the null hypothesis then you have shown the two means DO differ. If the above rule is not true then there is no statistically significant difference, no matter how different they look to you and you will ACCEPT the null hypothesis.

Here, your calculated value is 0.240. Your critical value is 2.074. Applying the rule, is $0.240 \geq 2.074$? NO. Therefore, the null hypothesis is supported - the two means are not different from one another. Stated yet another way, the mean birth weights for males and females, according to this data set, are not different.

Notice that in all this, what YOU think is true is not the basis for deciding. No matter whether you think males and females differ in weight or whether you think they don’t is not relevant. The statistical test has decided the answer for you.

A DIFFERENT QUESTION:

Suppose you see that there are three brands in the beer section of your local store. You become curious and want to know whether one brand is more popular than the others. Can you state the question in the form given above? How about, “What is the effect of brand of beer on its popularity?” or, to make the dependent variable more obvious, “What is the effect of brand of beer on the number of cans sold?” That means that brand of beer is the independent variable and we will measure the popularity of each brand by counting how many cans get sold. In this case, both the independent and the dependent variables are discrete. A can of beer is either Blitz OR Grog OR Zowie and you can only buy a can, not part of a can.

What experiment would you do? You could count the number of cans of each brand that get bought over several days. Suppose this is what you find:

Brand	Number Sold
Blitz	20
Grog	41
Zowie	27
TOTAL	88

So, 88 cans of beer were sold and the cans were DISTRIBUTED among the three brands in the way the table above shows. Is there a difference among the brands? You don't know until you do the statistics.

What are your hypotheses?

a) Your null hypothesis: All the brands are equally popular
b) Your alternative hypothesis: There is a difference in popularity between the brands.

What statistical test will let you choose between these two alternatives? You'd use the X^2 Test For Goodness of Fit. ("X^2" is also written "Chi" and is pronounced like the "ky" in "sky" so it's the "ky squared test" NOT the "ex-squared" test.) The rules that led us to this test are:

a) The dependent variable is composed of discrete data.
b) You are interested in how discrete objects are distributed in time or space.

What does the formula for the X^2 Test look like? Again, it's a series of steps that you follow according to the following formula:

$$X^2_{\text{(calculated)}} = \sum \frac{(\text{Observed value} - \text{Expected value})^2}{\text{Expected value}}$$

Okay, but what are our "observed" and "expected" values and what is that thing at the front of the formula? First, the "observed" values are the data you collected – the 27, 41 and 21 cans of beer sold among the three brands. Then what are the "expected" values? They are what you would expect IF the three brands were sold EXACTLY equally. In other words, they are the values you'd get if the null hypothesis were exactly correct.

	Blitz	Grog	Zowie	
observed	20	41	27	
expected	29.33	29.33	29.33	
obs.-exp.	-9.33	11.67	-2.33	
$(\text{obs.-exp.})^2$	87.05	136.19	5.43	
$\frac{(\text{obs.-exp.})^2}{\text{exp.}}$	2.97	4.64	0.19	$\sum = 7.80 = X^2$ calc.

That weird symbol at the front is "sigma". It says to go through the formula as many times as you have observed values (in this case that would be three times) and sum all of the $[(\text{obs-exp})^2/\text{exp}]$ values. That is, each time you get a value for $(\text{obs-exp})^2/\text{exp}$, you write it down. Then, when you have all those values, you add them together

How do you calculate the expected value? Since, in this case, your null says that the three brands are sold equally, you'd expect that, if this were the case, you'd find that 88/3 cans of each brand were sold. That would be 29.33 cans of beer for each brand. (Remember, this is the world of math so the expected can be fractional because of the way it is calculated. However, the observed cannot be a fraction since it is based on discrete items or categories.)

You simply take each observed and put it and its expected value in the formula, do the squaring and the division, then go on to do the same for the next observed value. You continue to do this until you run out of observed values. In our case, you'd do this 3 times, sum the three values and get:

$$X^2_{\text{(calculated)}} = \sum \frac{(27 - 29.33)^2}{29.33} + \frac{(41 - 29.33)^2}{29.33} + \frac{(20 - 29.33)^2}{29.33}$$

$= 7.80$

As before, we need to know two things: the degrees of freedom and the critical value. Again, you use the former to find the latter.

To get the degrees of freedom for X^2 Goodness of Fit take the number of levels of the independent variable and subtract 1. Here, the independent variable is "brand" and there are 3 levels: Blitz, Grog and Zowie. So, we have d.f. = 3 –1 = 2.

We take the number of degrees of freedom and go to Table 2 (page 21). In it, we see that the critical value associated with d.f. = 2 is 5.99.

Using the same rule we employed for the t-Test, we ask whether the calculated value is greater than or equal to the critical value. Is $7.194 \geq 5.99$? YES, and so in this case we REJECT the null hypothesis. We have demonstrated that there IS a difference in preference among the three brands sold at the store.

SUMMARY

From all this you should have learned several things. First, scientists are not afraid to ask what may seem like simple questions. More importantly, they are not afraid to try to answer them. Provisional answers to the questions are called hypotheses and these hypotheses are only useful if they are tested in experiments.

The data we collect in an experiment give us our dependent variable. The influence on the values that those dependent variables can have is called the independent variable.

Data can be of two types: Continuous or discrete. The types of data help determine which statistical test we will use to analyze our findings. We also need to know if we are looking for differences between means or if we are looking for differences between distributions.

The statistical test will tell us which of the hypotheses we can reject. The remaining one is the tentative answer to our question. Remember, though, we should repeat the experiment several times to be sure our answer is a reliable one. It's always possible that a single test of the hypothesis could just have accidentally given us a particular answer because the data we got were weird. The only way to make sure that our answer is robust and is really an accurate reflection of reality is to do the experiment several times.

EXERCISES. To see whether you understand what you have just read, try the following statistical exercises.

1) A farmer has a chicken feed salesman come up to him and the salesman says, "You should use Super Chicken feed because in a test run in our labs, we found that hens fed on Super Chicken weighed an average of 3.68 kg at the age of 8 weeks but hens on Funky Chicken only weighed an average of 3.43 kg." If you were the farmer, would you buy Super Chicken feed, based on this information? WHY?

2) Now, suppose you got your hands on the original data the salesman was quoting from. Here are the weights (in pounds), at age 8 weeks, of the chickens fed each type of feed:

Funky Chicken Feed		Super Chicken Feed	
3.97	2.99	3.44	5.03
4.17	3.11	2.39	3.17
2.68	3.65	4.23	3.82

a) Put the question being asked into the form used above ("What is the effect of…")
b) What is your dependent variable?
c) What type of data does the dependent variable represent?
d) What is your independent variable?
e) What type of data does your independent variable represent?
f) Is this a question of the difference between two means or does it deal with differences between distributions?
g) Which statistical test is the appropriate one and WHY is that the case?
h) Do the test and answer your question. With this answer, what would you say to the salesman?

3) Jeremiah was a bullfrog. You kept him for many years in an aquarium where he had several spots he could crawl out of the water and sit for food. One spot was a mound of earth in the left-hand corner, another was on a piece of wood in the middle of the tank and the third was a rock in the right-hand corner. Over a five-day period you noted where Jeremiah was sitting each time you left for school and again when you got home. Here's what you found:

Left Corner	Middle of Tank	Right Corner
12	21	29

So, did Jeremiah have a favored spot?

a) Put the question into the model given above.

b) What is your dependent variable?

c) What type of data does your dependent variable represent?

d) What is your independent variable?

e) What type of data does the independent variable represent?

f) Is this a question of the difference between means or is it one concerning differences in distributions?

g) What is the appropriate statistical test and WHY?

h) Do the test and answer the question.

4) After you graduate from Winthrop you join the Peace Corps and you end up in Botswana. There you see a graceful species of gazelle, the impala. They intrigue you and on your days off you watch them feed and move about. You realize that they occur in two areas, the open plains and the open woodland. Hearkening back to BIOL 150/151, you decide to see if they are more common in one habitat than they are in the other. You count them in each type of habitat in three locations and here' what you find:

Location	Open Plains	Open Woodland
1	16	27
2	44	34
3	32	39

So, are they more often found in one habitat than the other? Use what you did in the above questions to answer this one.

5) You really like Botswana and you give up your dreams of opening a pearl-diving school to stay and study impalas. It appears to you that some males are more successful at gaining mates than are others. Your impression is that males with horns longer than 100 cm have larger harems than do those with shorter horns. You look at the number of females per male for the two groups of males. Here's what you find:

Number of Females Per Male For Males With Horns < 100 CM	Number of Females Per Male For Males With Horns > 100 CM
4	13
8	10
3	9
10	16
7	12
8	11
9	9
6	8
	14

So, do males with longer horns have more females in their harems? Again, follow the steps outlined in questions 2 and 3 above in order to answer this question. You should also re-read the rules about types of data to make sure you have a firm grasp of this problem.

TABLE 1. Critical values for the t-Test.

Degrees of Freedom	Critical Value	Degrees of Freedom	Critical Value
1	12.706	17	2.110
2	4.303	18	2.101
3	3.182	19	2.093
4	2.776	20	2.086
5	2.571	21	2.080
6	2.447	22	2.074
7	2.365	23	2.069
8	2.306	24	2.064
9	2.262	25	2.060
10	2.228	26	2.056
11	2.201	27	2.052
12	2.179	28	2.048
13	2.160	29	2.045
14	2.145	30	2.042
15	2.131	40	2.021
16	2.120	60	2.000

TABLE 2. Critical values for the X^2 Test Chi-square test

Degrees of Freedom	Critical Value	Degrees of Freedom	Critical Value
1	3.84	16	26.29
2	5.99	17	27.58
3	7.81	18	28.87
4	9.49	19	30.14
5	11.07	20	31.41
6	12.59	21	32.67
7	14.07	22	33.92
8	15.51	23	35.17
9	16.92	24	36.42
10	18.31	25	37.65
11	19.68	30	43.77
12	21.03	35	49.80
13	22.36	40	55.75
14	23.69	45	61.65
15	25.00	50	67.51

Chi-Squared Test M & M Example

Sometimes in a chi-squared test, you are **given** an expected value (instead of calculating total observations/ # of levels), and you need to compare those expected values with your observed data.

For instance, if you are given a sample of M and M candy, the colors are not expected to be distributed evenly. If you visit the M and M website (http://us.mms.com/us/about/products/milkchocolate/), it claims the following distribution.

13% Brown 14% Yellow 13% Red 16% Green 24% Blue 20% Orange

Perhaps, you want to test your M and M sample against the expected distribution. You can collect some data and perform the Chi-Squared test to do so.

First of all, what would be your null hypothesis?

The M and M website [illegible] distribution claims are true.

What about your alternative hypothesis?

____

____

EXAMPLE PROBLEM: 54 random M&Ms are observed for color.
You are given the expected value for each color in percentages, so you will still need a little math to determine EXPECTED values for each color.

Think of it this way. Out of the 54 M and Ms you have, you expect 13% of them to be brown, so you will multiply total # M&Ms observed by % expected.
(BROWN= 54 X 0.13=7.02)

Complete the table from the information given, and reject or accept the null hypothesis.

M&M Color	Brown	Yellow	Red	Green	Blue	Orange	Total
Observed	13	10 7.56	5	13	5	8	54
Expected	7.02	[illegible]	2.7	7.02	2.7	4.32	(should=54*)
O-E	0	0	0	0	0	0	(should =0*)
$(O-E)^2$							
$(O-E)^2$ / E							$\Sigma = X^2 =$

(*as a check) d.f.=__________ Critical Value=___________ REJECT or ACCEPT ??

ONCE YOUR ANSWER IS CORRECT, OBTAIN YOUR OWN M&Ms TO TEST.
Hint: be careful; your expected values will probably differ from the example!

M&M Color	Brown	Yellow	Red	Green	Blue	Orange	Total
Observed							
Expected							(should=total*)
O-E							(should =0*)
$(O-E)^2$							
$(O-E)^2$ / E							$\sum = X^2 =$

(*as a check) d.f.=_________ Critical Value=__________ REJECT or ACCEPT ??

QUESTION FOR THOUGHT: How might a larger sample size affect your results?

QUESTION TO TRY: Combine the class data (observation data) to see if it affects your results.

4 ANIMAL BEHAVIOR (by William Rogers, PhD.)

Objectives

After completing this unit you will be able to:

- Understand what we mean by "animal behavior"
- Understand how we study animal behavior
- Carry out an animal behavior study of your own design

Introduction

What Is Animal Behavior?

One of the most important characteristics of animals is that they can move themselves, often quickly or over great distances. This allows an individual to change locations or to manipulate the environment for its own benefit. While other organisms have similar abilities (single-celled protozoa can also move and even plants can bend toward light or away from gravity), animals can move farther, faster and with greater precision than can the members of any other kingdom.

"Animal behavior" is based on this ability to move and to move dramatically. Movement allows animals to seek food, water, shelter, mates and all the other things that they need to complete their life cycles. So, we can define "animal behavior" as muscle-based movements of the body or parts of the body by individual animals. That may sound too weak to cover the full range of things you might put under the category of behavior but think about anything you have ever seen one of your pets do. Your cat walks or runs to its food dish; it yowls to you, telling you it wants to be fed, using a muscle called the diaphragm to force air through its larynx; it moves its jaws to chew. The cat used muscle movements to get to its food, to communicate its hunger to you and to bring the food into its body. Apply this exercise to any other animal you can think of.

Notice that in order to do these complex things, the cat also has to have a central processor of information – a brain. The brain lets the cat bring in information from the environment. The brain can also retain the information and can make connections between what the animal perceives now and what it has experienced earlier in its life. Those abilities are the bases for particularly complicated behavior, such things as problem-solving and insight learning, things that large-brained organisms can do.

However, while all animals behave, not all are capable of such complicated actions. The ability to have complex behavior is an adaptation and species differ in how involved their behavior can be. Because the most costly cells in an animal's body are neurons (= nerve cells), if members of a species survive and reproduce just as well with simpler brains and thus simpler actions, there is no basis for evolving more complex behavior; why maintain expensive, complicated machinery unless there's an advantage to do so? That's part of the reason animal species do not all have the same behavioral repertoires.

How Do We Study Animal Behavior?

How does an ethologist, someone interested in animal behavior (or "ethology") go about studying it? To study anything, we need not only definitions but also units. Units allow us to break something complex into useful, manageable elements. In ethology we call these units action patterns. Action patterns are repeated, stereotyped movements and postures. Ethologists find action patterns by first watching what an animal does and looking for repeated activities. Then they carefully define and name these actions and use them to investigate particular questions about the animal's behavior. Let's use an example to illustrate this process.

Suppose you notice some squirrels on the campus are gathering food. You might think that the "food-gathering" would be a single activity but if you looked carefully at what the animals are doing you'd see that their feeding behavior is really composed of a series of separate actions. These actions are based on various postures and movements. For example, you might first see a squirrel as it walks on all four legs; its back would be parallel to the ground, sort of in the position a dog uses as it ambles along. At certain points a squirrel might stop and sit, changing both its movement and posture. It might then look around as it sits or it might lean forward and move its front paws as it digs in the soil. If it finds something to eat, the squirrel will likely go through another series of actions as it sniffs or manipulates the food item. Finally it might begin to gnaw on whatever it found. All these actions are associated with foraging or food-gathering.

Each action, if defined clearly, would be recognizable to another person also studying squirrel behavior. Remember, a hallmark of science is that experiments and observations have to be repeatable by other workers. Unless another person can unambiguously tell what you did, your work is not good science. So how would you define these actions or other actions associated with feeding? You might do something like this:

Slow walk: The squirrel moves on all four feet without jumping or bounding. The back is always parallel to the ground.

Run: The squirrel moves with a series of bounds or jumps, sometimes interspersed with steps.

Scan: The squirrel sits upright and turns its head from side to side.

Dig: The squirrel uses its front paws as it excavates soil.

Sniff: The squirrel brings a food item up to its face but does not bite it.

Work Food: The squirrel manipulates the object, turning it around.

Bite: The squirrel opens its mouth and brings the food into contact with its teeth.

Each of these is an action pattern, a definable unit of behavior. Note that we try to simply describe WHAT the animal does but we avoid saying WHY it does the action. By avoiding the "why" we allow ourselves to approach an animal's behavior without preconceived ideas about its behavior. Such caution prevents us from letting our prejudices determine our conclusions. Taking such care at the start allows new, unexpected ideas and interpretations to emerge. We interpret what we have seen only after we have observed carefully and analyzed the data that emerge from our observations.

What Do Ethologists Do With Such Information?

As is true for all scientists, ethologists ask questions, do experiments and look for patterns that emerge from their results as well as from the results of other ethological studies. Some ethologists are interested in the comparative approach, which contrasts how different species go about given tasks. For example, you might ask whether the many species of squirrels all forage in the same way; similarly, you might ask whether squirrels and monkeys use the same sorts of behaviors to find food. In either case, the pattern of similarities and differences will tell you much about WHY the animals do what they do.

Alternatively, you might simply be interested in a particular species and you might want to characterize all or specific features of its behavior. Abandoning squirrels, you might be interested in how close robins let people get near them. Do they allow a closer approach if the robin is alone as opposed to being in a flock? Do they let people without dogs get closer than folks with dogs? Do they allow people to get closer when the birds are in open places (such as Peabody Field) as opposed to more wooded locations (such as on the Oakland Avenue side of the campus)?

The list of questions that can be asked is limited only by your imagination. However, answering any ethological question depends on asking the question clearly and on defining the action patterns that will be recorded and analyzed.

Potential Exercises in Ethology

Below, you will find possible behavioral observation exercises. These are divided into non-human and human categories. In either case, to answer a question based on your own ideas or on any of these suggestions, you need to follow the following steps:

1) Ask the question so that it is clear and understandable. Be specific. Ask something like, "Does the size of a mockingbird's territory depend on the number of plants it controls?" rather than "What is the relationship between plants and mockingbird territories?" The first question makes the dependent and independent variables clear. In the second one the independent variable is really not stated. It could be plant number OR it could be plant type OR plant size, etc.

2) Keep the question simple. Don't try to involve more than one dependent or more than one independent variable. Scientists do ask such questions but they are complicated. You won't have time to do a good job on those sorts of questions in this class.

3) Take the question and put it into the model given to you in the Statistics chapter: "What is the effect of ___________ on ___________?" This will help you see what you are dealing with and it will help you make sure you understand the question, establish the variables, determine the statistical test, etc.

4) Come up with your hypotheses and *identify your working hypothesis.* Be sure to be able to defend your hypotheses, especially your working hypothesis.

5) Think about what data you need to collect and how you will gather them. This will take some time. THINK about WHEN you have to do collect the data, HOW MUCH TIME it will take, HOW OFTEN you need to gather data, HOW TO MAKE SURE NO OTHER VARIABLES will affect your data, WHAT EXACTLY your data will be, etc. If you can go out and spend just an hour or so doing a "pilot experiment" where you try out your data gathering methods you will get a much better picture of what you a re proposing to do and you may find that your methods need adjusting.

6) Put an honest effort into gathering the data. Be sure to leave time to do the statistics and to THINK about what the answers you got mean.

Sample Topics

A. Non-human animals

1.Mockingbird territorial behavior

2. Ant trail formation/maintenance

3. Spacing of robins on lawns

4. Squirrel foraging behavior

B. Human behaviors

1. Individual actions:

a. Stopping at STOP signs: sex/age class differences

b. Seatbelt use.: sex/age class differences

c. The directions people turn when first entering a setting (beach, mall, movie theater, etc.)

d. Food choices in the cafeteria: sex/race comparisons

2. Social behaviors

a. Affiliative behaviors at McFeat Developmental School - Who associates with whom?

b. Group sizes: sex/race differences

c. Mother/infant relationships at a mall

d. Activity types among kids at McFeat Developmental School

3. Sexual behaviors

a. Hand-holding - whose hand is on top; who initiates; whose right hand is used, etc.

b. Assortative vs. non-assortative mating – do people of one sort (age/height/hair color, etc) tend to pair up with people like them or different from them?

EXPERIMENTAL DESIGN WORKSHEET

DATE________ GROUP: ________________________

____

____

____

1) QUESTION: ____

2) HYPOTHESES:
   a) NULL: ____
   b) ALTERNATIVE #1: __________________________________
   c) ALTERNATIVE #2: __________________________________

3) YOUR WORKING HYPOTHESIS: ______________________________

4) VARIABLES:
   a) INDEPENDENT: ____________________________________
   b) DEPENDENT: ______________________________________
   c) CONTROLLED:______________________________________

5) DATA TYPE FOR DEPENDENT VARIABLE:________________________

6) METHODS:
   a) Exactly WHAT will you measure and how? (Continue on back if necessary)

   ____

   ____

   ____

   ____

   b) How often will you measure this?

   ____

   ____

   ____

   c) What is your proposed sample size? ________________________

   ____

   d) What statistical test will you use to analyze your results? Why? ___________

   ____

   ____

5 ECOLOGY CONCEPTS

Objectives

After completing this unit you will be able to:

- explain the role of producers, consumers, decomposers and abiotic material in the ecosystem
- explain the relationship between photosynthesis and cellular respiration
- determine the trophic level to which each organism belongs
- explain how energy *flows* and nutrients *cycle* through the ecosystem

Introduction

Ecology is the study of the interaction between living organisms and their physical environment. The word ecology is derived from the Greek word *oikos* which means house.

The **ecosystem** is the combination of a community of living organisms and their environment. A **community** consists of all the populations of all the species occupying a given area at a given time. A **population** is a group of individuals of the same species occupying a given area at a given time.

The **habitat** is the place where an individual organism occupies and includes the physical and chemical features as well as the other organisms present.

I. Producers

Green plants are the producers in a community. Plants convert the sun's light energy to chemical energy. Animals cannot convert light energy to chemical energy and must obtain energy directly or indirectly from plants.

A. Chloroplast Structure

Photosynthesis is the process by which plants convert light energy into chemical energy. Photosynthesis occurs in plant organelles called "**chloroplasts**." (*Figure 40.1*). Chloroplasts contain the pigment chlorophyll that traps the sun's energy.

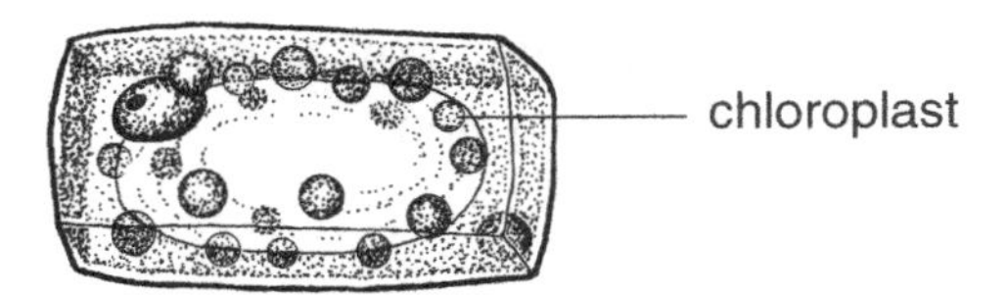

Figure 40.1 Elodea cell showing chloroplasts

B. Examples of Producers

1. Spirogyra is a floating filamentous green algae containing chlorophyll in chloroplasts arranged in a spiral. *Spirogyra* forms a bright green frothy mass on or just below the water surface. The slimy feel is caused by a watery sheath surrounding each filament.

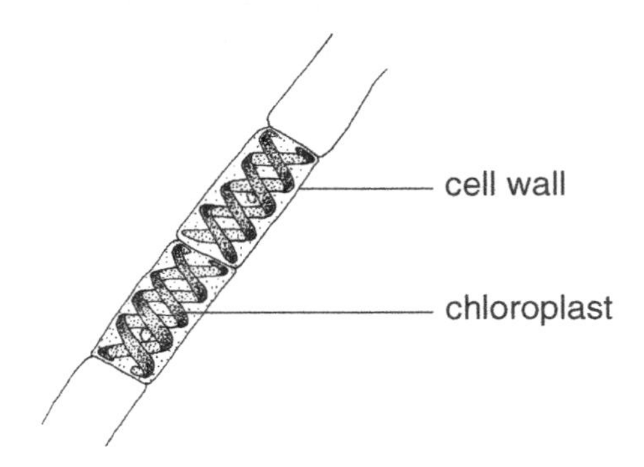

Figure 40.2 Spirogyra

2. Volvox is a motile colonial green algae. The colonies are photosynthetic and appear as green spheres. Each colony is a hollow cluster of cells that are held together by a gelatinous matrix. Each cell has flagella that beat, causing the colony to roll through the water. They reproduce by daughter cells, which develop into their own spheres inside the colony.

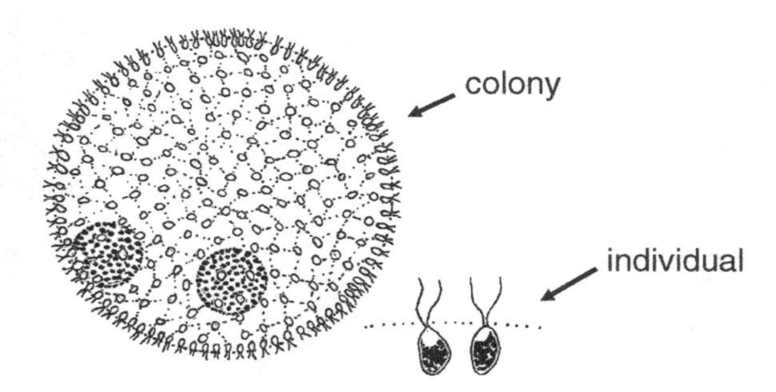

Figure 40.3 Volvox

3. Elodea is a common vascular aquatic plant. Vascular plants have conducting tissue that transports substances from cell to cell. The cells of *Elodea* leaves are only a few layers thick. The chloroplasts in *Elodea* cells can easily be viewed with the microscope.

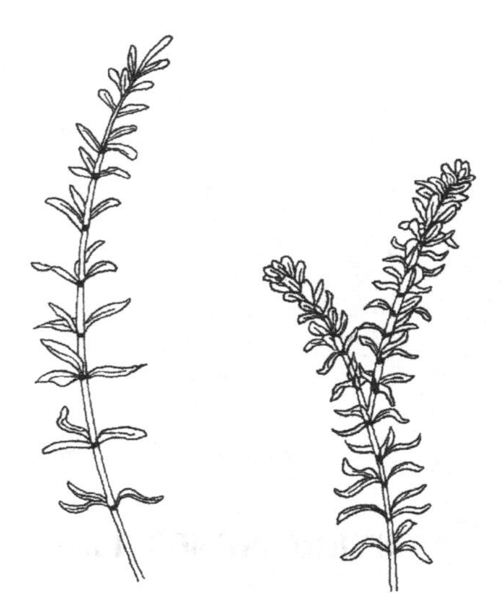

Figure 40.4 Elodea

4. A **fern** is a vascular plant that can be found growing in moist shaded areas. Ferns have horizontal stems that grow close to the ground and attached leaves that are called fronds. Ferns

produce spores from reproductive structures located on the underside of the fronds.

Figure 40.5 Fern

5. Geraniums are common flowering plants. Their leaves contain aromatic oils that give this plant its characteristic scent. The chloroplasts are concentrated in the upper layers of the leaf cells for efficient energy production.

Figure 40.6 Geranium

EXERCISE 40.1 Identification of producers

1. Observe the samples of producers displayed in the laboratory.

2. Record the name of the specimen in *Table 40.1*. For each specimen, identify distinguishing characteristics and the reasons why it is a producer.

Organism	Characteristics	Why is this a Producer?

Table 40.1 Examples of producers

3. Prepare a wet mount of *Elodea* leaf. Place a drop of pond water on a clean glass slide. Place one leaf in the drop of water and cover it with a cover slip. Observe the slide under the microscope. The leaf is more than one cell layer thick. Focus on one cell layer.

- What are the disk-shaped green structures in the leaf cells? What is their function?

II. Consumers

Consumers depend on other organisms for glucose, amino acids, and other organic molecules. **Primary consumers (herbivores)** eat plant material. **Secondary consumers (carnivores)** eat primary consumers. Organisms that utilize living tissue for their nourishment **(parasites)** are also considered secondary consumers.

Examples of Consumers

1. Paramecia are unicellular protozoa, which ingest algae and other unicellular organisms. They sweep food into an oral opening called a oral groove. From there the food enters the gullet where it will become enclosed by an enzyme-containing food vacuole. Paramecium move by beating the cilia that line the body surface.

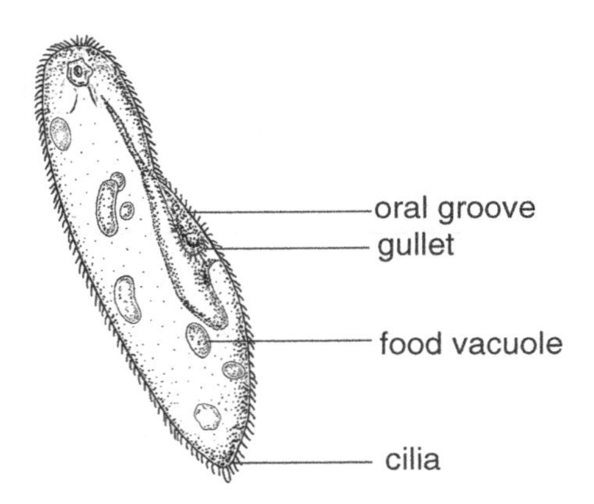

Figure 40.7 Paramecium

2. Honey bees are colonial insects that obtain food from the pollen of flowering plants. There is a close relationship between bees and flowering plants. Bees rely on flowers for their food supply, and the flowers depend on bees to carry pollen from one flower to the next for cross fertilization. A single queen bee lays all the eggs in a bee colony. The worker bees collect pollen, convert it to honey and feed the honey to developing larvae. Honey bees have three stages to their life cycle: egg, larvae and adult.

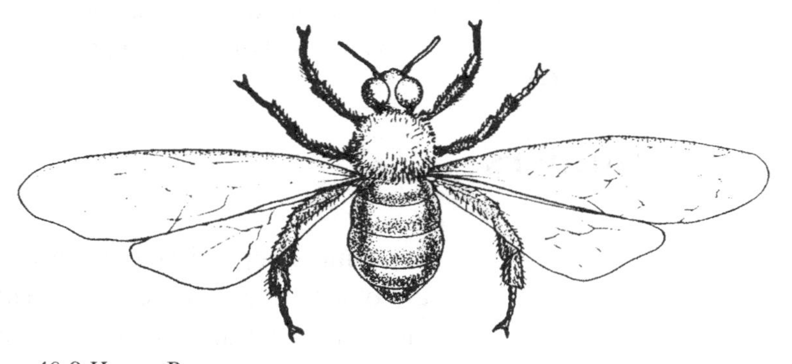

Figure 40.8 Honey Bee

3. Perch are carnivorous fish which eat mosquitoes and other insects. They have numerous small sharp teeth extending from the roof of the mouth and jawbone. The teeth slant toward the throat to prevent prey from escaping. Some carnivorous fish such as bass swallow fish almost as large as themselves. Since the esophagus and stomach are in a straight line, digestion can begin before the prey is completely swallowed.

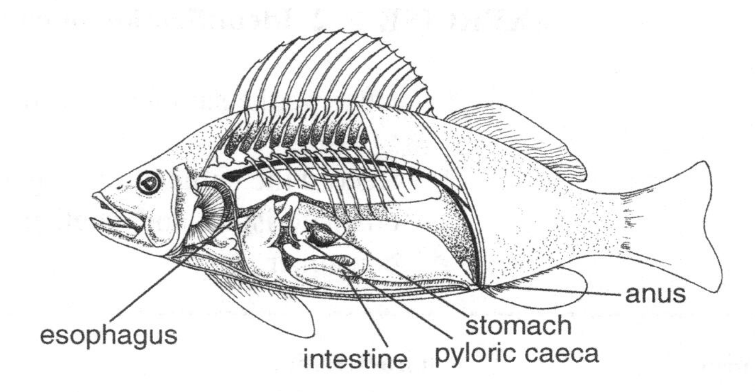

Figure 40.9 Perch

4. Frogs begin life as tadpoles. During this stage of their development, they are aquatic and breathe with gills. They are herbivores. The mouth parts and intestinal tract are adapted to a plant diet. After metamorphosis, the frog becomes terrestrial and breathes with lungs. Adult frogs are carnivores with mouth parts and intestines adapted to a diet of other animals. Their diet consists primarily of insects and worms. A thick sticky tongue is attached to the floor of the mouth at the front. Two vomerine teeth project from the bones in the roof of the mouth and aid in holding the prey.

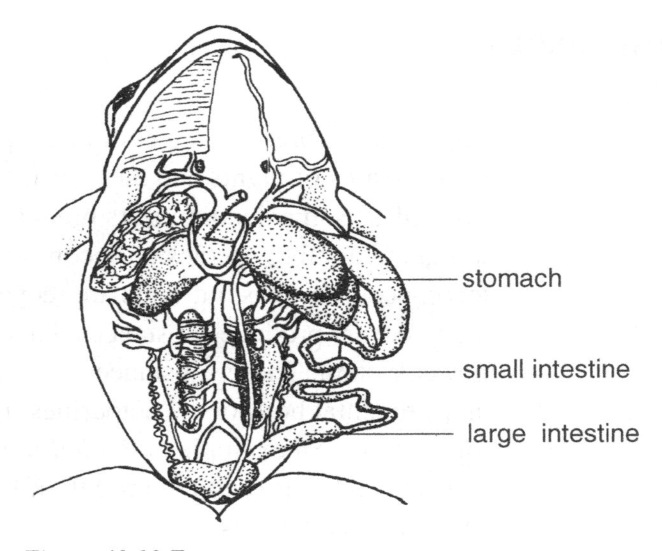

Figure 40.10 Frog

EXERCISE 40.2 Identification of consumers

1. Observe the samples of consumers displayed in the lab.

2. Record the name of the organism, its distinguishing characteristics, and whether it is a primary or secondary consumer.

Organism	Characteristics	Identify the type of consumer

Table 40.2 Consumers

III. Decomposers

Decomposers break down complex organic molecules found in the dead remains of plants and animals into simple inorganic molecules. Some decomposers breakdown a substance to one point, and another species of decomposer then continues decomposition, thus nutrients are recycled in the ecosystem. Some decomposers produce substances that exert a regulatory control in the ecosystem. These substances are called **ectocrines** or environmental hormones. Ectocrines limit the growth of other populations. An example is *Penicillium*, a mold that releases a substance inhibitory to the growth of bacteria. Many antibiotics function as ectocrines.

This process begins when plants lose leaves or die and animals excrete wastes or die. The major decomposers are **bacteria** and **fungi** living in sediments or soils where organic debris accumulates.

The basic elements of living systems are carbon, hydrogen, oxygen, and nitrogen. These are taken up as plant nutrients in the form of carbon dioxide, water, nitrate, and phosphate. These substances then pass from one level of the ecosystem to the next in the form of organic molecules. Eventually, the decomposers return them as mineral nutrients to the air, water, and soil to be used again by plants. Thus, materials are recycled over and over again in the ecosystem.

Examples of Decomposers

1. Bacteria are one-celled prokaryotic organisms. They are the major decomposers of any ecosystem. Prokaryotes are one-celled organisms without a membrane-bound nucleus or other internal organelles. They have the ability to reduce organic materials to inorganic molecules that plants in the ecosystem can then use again.

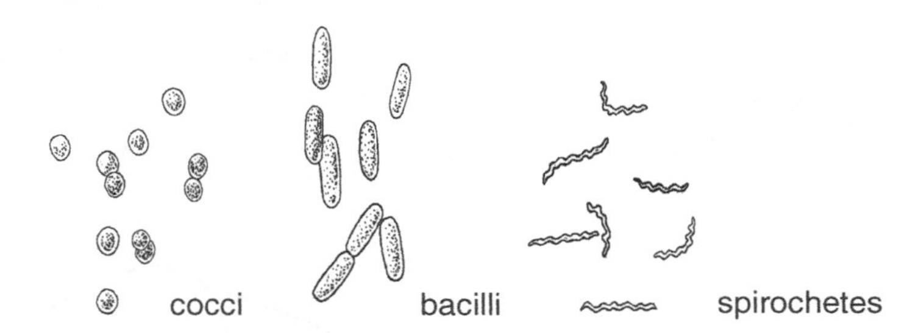

Figure 40.11 Three shapes of bacteria

2. Fungi are a group of heterotrophs without roots, stems, leaves, or flowers. These organisms include yeast, mold, mildew, mushrooms, and rust. Some fungi are parasites while others are decomposers and feed upon dead organic matter.

   The two primary tasks for fungi are absorbing nutrients and reproducing. The **mycelium** is the food absorbing body of a fungus. It consists of a network of branching microscopic filaments. Each filament is called a **hypha**. Most hyphae are composed of elongated cells surrounded by chitin-reinforced walls. The hypha grows over the material containing nutrients. Digestion occurs outside of the hypha by cellular secretion of digestive enzymes. The nutrients are then absorbed and transported from one region to another by cytoplasmic movements. In many species of fungi, some of the hypha are modified into reproductive structures where spores or gametes develop.

Bread mold often grows on stale baked goods (*Figure 40.12*). The mycelium consists of many hyphae. The rootlike hyphae that penetrate the food supply are called **rhizoids**. Rhizoids anchor the mycelium to the substance. They also produce enzymes that are secreted into the surrounding organic material. These enzymes break down the material into simpler compounds that are absorbed across the cell membrane of the rhizoids. Eventually, these nutrients will be returned to the soil.

Specialized hyphae called **sporangiophores** are elevated above the surface of the food supply and support the **sporangia**. Each sporangium is a container of spores. The spores are airborne, asexual reproductive cells that give rise to hyphae of a new mycelium.

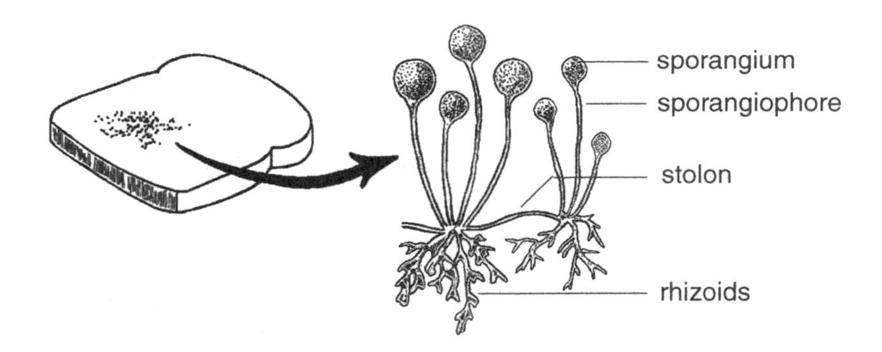

Figure 40.12 Bread mold mycelium with sporangia

Mushrooms are another group of decomposers (*Figure 40.13*). Most species get nutrients from plant debris. The mycelium, the vegetative portion of the mushroom, consists of hyphae that spread through soil or the wood of a decaying log. When conditions are ideal, the fruiting body, the **basidiocarp** bearing large numbers of spores, becomes visible. The basidiocarp consists of a stalk and cap. The numerous sheets of tissue hanging from the lower surface are called gills. The gills produce reproductive cells called **basidiospores**. In addition to their role as a decomposer, mushrooms contribute to the aeration of soil.

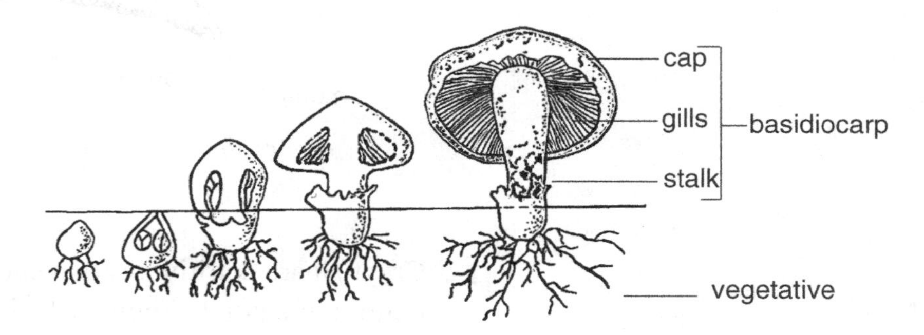

Figure 40.13 Mushroom development

3. Detritivores are decomposers that feed on particles of organic matter that are produced by the partial decomposition of plant and animal tissues. Examples include earthworms, nematodes, crabs, and crayfish.

   Earthworms are detritivores that obtain materials and energy from dead plant material on the surface of the ground (*Figure 40.14*). At night the worm comes to the surface and feeds on soil that contains decomposing organic matter. Soil enters the digestive tract by the suction of the muscular pharynx. The food then passes through the esophagus. Behind the esophagus is the crop which serves as a temporary storage place and the gizzard which grinds up the food. Digestion and absorption occur in the intestine. The energy in complex organic molecules is utilized by the earthworm and eventually given off as heat. The worm excrement or castings are mostly abiotic material. Abiotic material is nonliving, inorganic material resulting from the breakdown of organic material. Worm castings are sold commercially as a fertilizer.

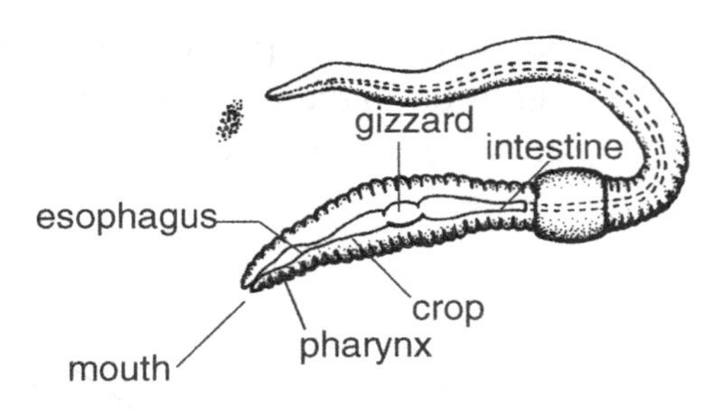

Figure 40.14 Earthworm

Crayfish are detritivores that eat dead remains that settle to the bottom of a pond (*Figure 40.15*). The chelipeds assist in obtaining food and protection. The maxillipeds hold the food while it is chewed by the mandibles. The food passes through the esophagus on the way to the stomach. The stomach is lined with teeth that grind the food into smaller pieces. The digested food enters the digestive glands where absorption takes place. Undigested food enters the intestine and is eliminated through the anus and is reused by producers.

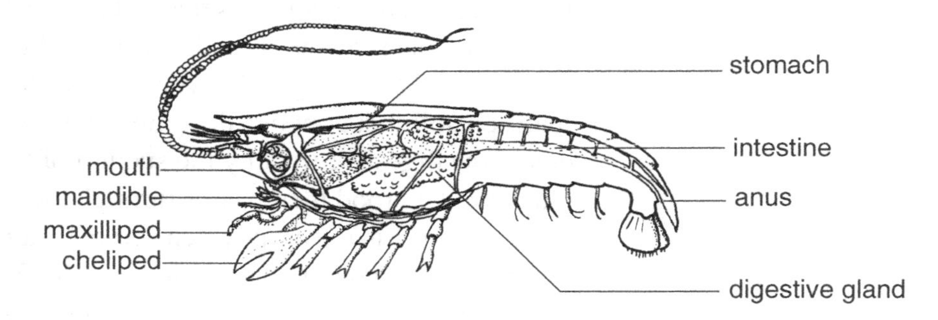

Figure 40.15 Crayfish

EXERCISE 40.3 Decomposers

1. Observe the samples of decomposers displayed in the lab.

2. In *Table 40.3*, record the name of the organism, its distinguishing characteristics, and why it is a decomposer.

Organism	Characteristics	Why is this a decomposer?

Table 40.3 Decomposers

IV. Abiotic Material

Abiotic materials in the ecosystem include **inorganic** compounds and ions such as water, carbon dioxide, nitrates, carbonates, and phosphates. Plants convert these inorganic compounds into the organic compounds of living tissues (carbohydrates, fats, proteins, and nucleic acids). When an organism dies, decomposers convert the organic compounds of its body into simple inorganic compounds.

V. Relationships Between Organisms

A. Vocabulary

Producers: Green plants, some protista, and some monera that convert light energy to chemical energy.

Primary consumers: Organisms that eat producers to obtain nutrients and energy. Primary consumers are called **herbivores**.

Secondary consumers: Organisms that eat primary consumers to obtain nutrients and energy. Secondary consumers are called **carnivores**.

Parasites: Organisms that obtain nutrients and energy from other living organisms by ingesting blood, sap, or other living tissues. Mosquitoes and tapeworms are examples.

Tertiary consumers: Organisms that eat secondary consumers to obtain nutrients and energy.

Omnivores: Organisms that obtain nutrients and energy from both plants and animals.

B. Energy Relationships

During **photosynthesis**, light energy is converted to chemical energy. A general equation summarizing photosynthesis is:

$$\underset{\text{carbon dioxide}}{6CO_2} + \underset{\text{water}}{6H_2O} \xrightarrow[\text{chlorophyll}]{\text{sunlight}} \underset{\text{glucose}}{C_6H_{12}O_6} + \underset{\text{oxygen}}{6O_2}$$

During **cellular respiration**, chemical energy is converted into ATP and heat energy. A summary equation for aerobic respiration is:

$$\underset{\text{glucose}}{C_6H_{12}O_6} + \underset{\text{oxygen}}{6O_2} \xrightarrow{\text{enzymes}} \underset{\text{carbon dioxide}}{6CO_2} + \underset{\text{water}}{6H_2O} + 36\ ATP$$

ATP is a high-energy molecule that supplies energy for all chemical processes that occur in cells. These processes are collectively called **metabolism**. Metabolism is the total chemical activity in the cell. (See *Figure 40.16*).

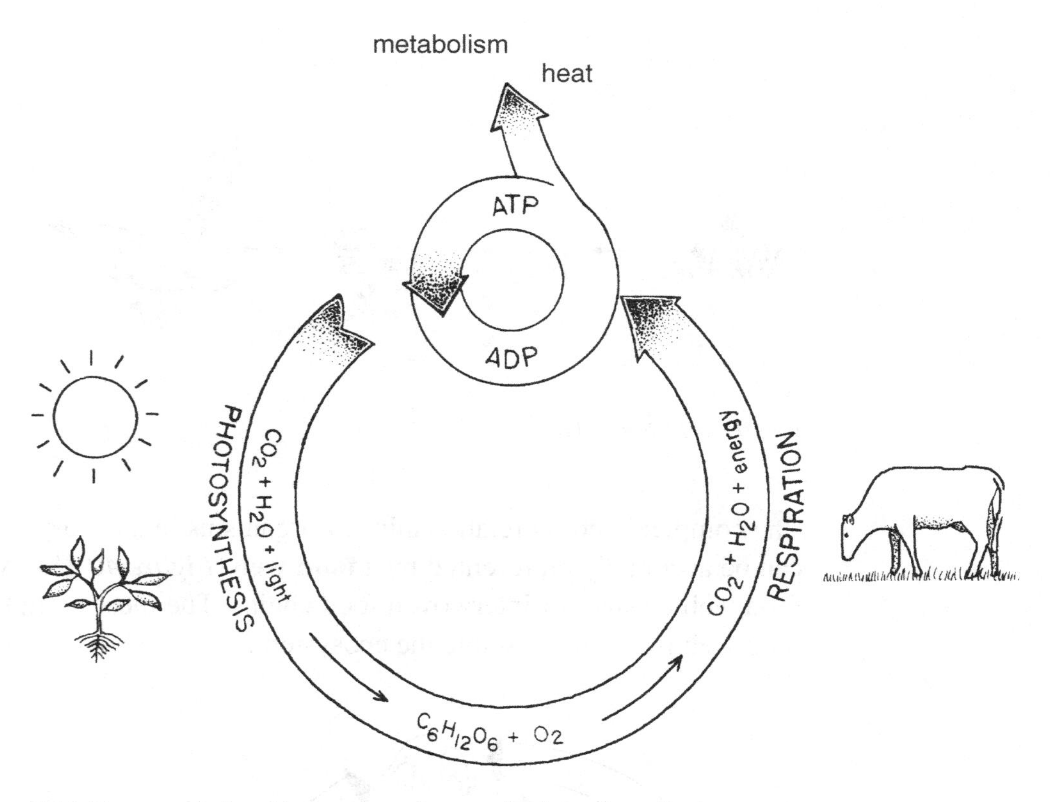

Figure 40.16 Energy relationship between photosynthesis and respiration

C. Trophic Levels

A **trophic level** is a feeding level that identifies an organism's energy source (who eats whom). Organisms are on the same trophic level if they share the same general source of food. A community may have four or five trophic levels, each level containing a variety of species. Examples of trophic levels are producers, primary consumers, secondary consumers, tertiary consumers, and decomposers. Decomposers break down the dead remains of organisms from each trophic level.

D. Food Chains and Food Webs

The transfer of materials and energy from one organism to another represents a simple feeding sequence or **food chain** (*Figure 40.17*). A food chain is an oversimplification of the feeding relationships in nature because organisms usually eat more than one type of food.

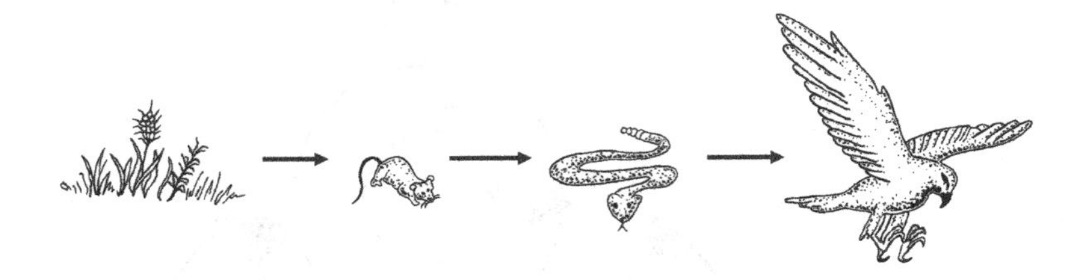

Figure 40.17 Food chain

The complex feeding relationships of organisms in an ecosystem can be accurately represented by a **food web** (*Figure 40.18*). A food web consists of interwoven food chains. The more complex a food web is, the more stable the ecosystem.

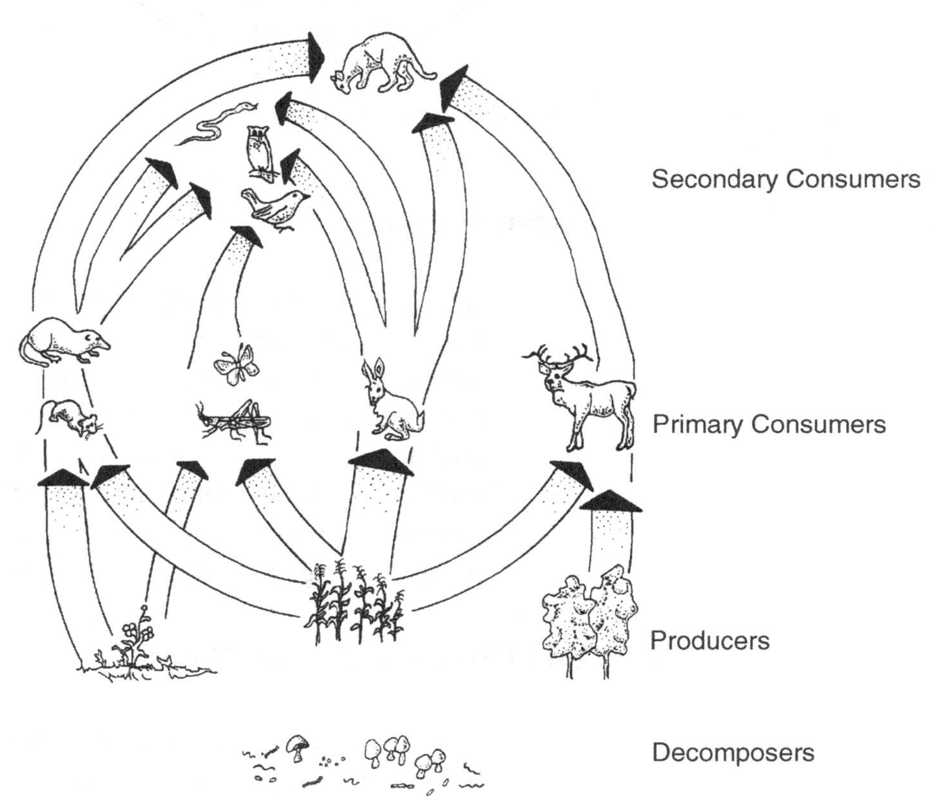

Figure 40.18 Food web

EXERCISE 40.4 Terrestrial ecosystem

1. Study the ecosystem represented in the above food web.
2. Name the producers, consumers, and decomposers.

   Producers:

   Consumers:

   Decomposers:

3. What are the abiotic components of an ecosystem?
4. Draw a single food chain using the organisms from the food web.
5. Identify the organisms that compete for food in the food web (*Figure 40.18*).

VI. Flow of Energy

The source of energy for most organisms is the sun. Plants receive light energy and convert a portion of it to chemical energy during photosynthesis. A portion of the energy stored in plant tissues is transferred when other organisms feed upon them. At each energy transfer or trophic level, heat energy is dissipated into the atmosphere and eventually into space. In the final conversion of organic materials to abiotic material by decomposers, the last of the chemical energy stored in organic molecules is converted to heat. Therefore, energy flows only once through the ecosystem. An ecosystem is considered **open** because an outside source of light energy must constantly replace the heat energy leaving the ecosystem.

An energy pyramid (*Figure 40.19*) can be used to show the transfer of energy in an ecosystem. As energy is transferred from one organism to the next in a food chain, each succeeding level represents a **trophic level**. In an energy pyramid the plants (primary producers at the base of the pyramid), trap light energy and convert it to chemical energy that is transferred from one trophic level to the next. The decomposers are not shown on this pyramid, but they are at work breaking down the remains and wastes of each trophic level.

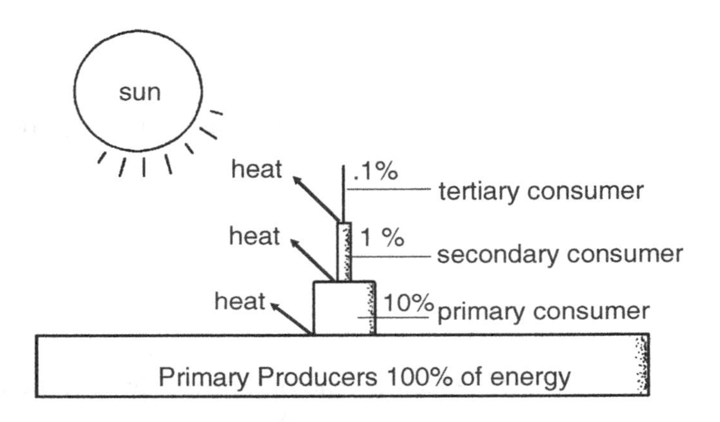

Figure 40.19 Energy pyramid

A **primary producer** (plant) is able to capture **1-2%** of the light energy falling on the surface of a leaf. This energy is converted to chemical energy (glucose) that can be converted to ATP during cellular respiration. A primary consumer can capture approximately **10%** of the energy stored in the body of the plants it eats. The other **90%** is dissipated into space as heat. At each succeeding trophic level, about **10%** of the energy in the food source is available. The rest of the energy is dissipated as low-grade heat during cellular respiration.

In summary, energy enters the ecosystem in the form of sunlight. Energy flows through the ecosystem by way of food webs. Energy leaves the ecosystem as low-grade heat at each trophic level.

EXERCISE 40.5 Energy flow in the ecosystem

- How much of the producer's energy is captured by secondary consumers?

- An **omnivore**, such as a bear, can obtain nutrition by eating plant material or animal material. From an energy standpoint, which source most efficiently utilizes the sun's energy?

- Explain how vegetarians obtain energy in the energy pyramid.

VII. Cycling of Materials

Materials cycle through the ecosystem continuously. All organisms are made up of complex organic molecules but only photosynthetic plants are capable of synthesizing these from inorganic materials. Therefore, all ecosystems ultimately depend on green plants for their existence. Plants utilize light energy from the sun to synthesize organic molecules from CO_2 (carbon dioxide), H_2O (water), and minerals. Plants then serve as food for the primary consumers. The primary consumers in turn become food for secondary consumers. The decomposers break down the dead remains and wastes from organisms at each trophic level. They break down complex organic materials into inorganic molecules. These inorganic molecules are returned to the soil and are then available to new plants. Therefore, materials are recycled in the ecosystem. An ecosystem is **closed** in terms of materials.

- Which organisms break down organic molecules into inorganic molecules?

- Name three molecules that cycle through living systems.

Summary Questions

_____________________ 1. All the organisms of the same species in one location.

_____________________ 2. What is the term for the place where an organism lives?

_____________________ 3. What is the term for a community and its physical and chemical environment?

_____________________ 4. Give an example of a parasite.

_____________________ 5. Give an example of a producer.

_____________________ 6. Give an example of a detritivore.

_____________________ 7. What are the two major groups of decomposers in an ecosystem?

____

_____________________ 8. What is another term for primary consumer?

_____________________ 9. What is another term for secondary consumer?

_____________________ 10. What term best describes the eating pattern of humans?

11. Explain how energy enters, flows through, and exits an ecosystem.

12. Explain how materials cycle in the ecosystem.

Photosynthesis and Respiration Lab
Compiled by Biology 151 Staff

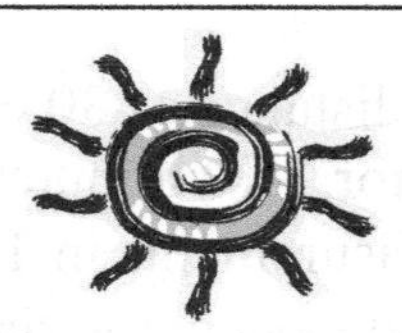

Introductory Questions

- What is the general equation for photosynthesis?
- What does this mean in words?
- If we wanted to know if photosynthesis is occurring, what evidence could we look for?

In this laboratory investigation, we will look for this evidence in several different situations. *You will be working together with both your lab group and another lab group to collect data.*

Part I. Effect of Light on Photosynthesis

Background: The amount of sunlight striking Earth's surface changes throughout the day, from week to week, and during the year. Since oxygen is a product of photosynthesis, measuring or counting the release of oxygen bubbles from a plant may be used to test the effect of varying light intensity.

Purpose: In this experiment, a cutting of an aquatic plant, *Anacharis,* will be placed into a solution of sodium bicarbonate ($NaHCO_3$) at varying distances from a constant light source.

Problem: From this information, what is the basic question we will be asking?

What is the effect of

____?

- What is the independent variable, and what is the dependent variable in this experiment?
- What should be controlled variables? (constants)

(Make a hypothesis before you start collecting data. It should include information to back up your prediction.)

HYPOTHESIS

=____

____

Procedure

- After system is equilibrated (with the light at a distance of 50 cm from the plant for at least 7-10 minutes), determine the rate of photosynthesis by counting the bubbles produced each minute for a five-minute period (Table 1), and then find the average bubble count per minute.
- Move the lamp to a distance of 30 cm, and allow the system to equilibrate AGAIN for 7-10 minutes.
- Repeat the same measurements in Table 1 for the distance of 30 cm.
- For the graph, the independent variable goes on the X axis and the dependent variable goes on the Y axis. Make sure you label each axis with measurement AND unit. Do not connect the dots, but draw a straight best-fit line between the points. (Ask your instructor/GA to clarify.)

RESULTS

Table 1

Distance from light (cm)	# bubbles after 1st minute	# bubbles after 2nd minute	# bubbles after 3rd minute	# bubbles after 4th minute	# bubbles after 5th minute	AVERAGE BUBBLE COUNT / MINUTE
50						
30						
10						

Figure 1 Effect of Light Intensity on Photosynthesis

CONCLUSION QUESTIONS

1. Why must you allow the system to equilibrate for 7-10 minutes before starting to count bubbles at EACH distance?

2. Does your prediction appear to be correct? Explain. If not, speculate what may have happened.

3. Why is it necessary to add the bicarbonate to the system?

4. Why did we measure both bubbles per minute and volume of oxygen?

5. Could we perform the t-test or chi-squared test with this data? Explain.

Part II. Testing for Presence of Starch

BACKGROUND

When an abundance of glucose is formed in the plant (such as the leaf), it is often converted into starch for energy storage.

Glucose molecule (monomer)= ⬡
Starch (many glucose molecules/polymer) =
⬡- ⬡- ⬡- ⬡- ⬡- ⬡- ⬡- ⬡- ⬡- ⬡- ⬡- ⬡- ⬡- ⬡-
We can use iodine to test for starch; it reacts to form a bluish-black color.
For example, a potato is full of starch.

- On a paper towel, add a few drops of iodine (IKI) to your potato slice to see the color appear. ***(Be careful, iodine can stain skin and clothes).***

Purpose:

In this experiment, you will use two geranium plants that have been previously exposed to two different levels of light, and you will test them for the presence of starch.

Plant A- has been in full light for the past seven days with one leaf partially covered by foil
Plant B- has been in the dark for the past seven days with one leaf partially covered by foil

Both plants were in the greenhouse before the experiment began and cared for the same way. During the experiment, both plants were watered at the same time.

Problem:

From this information, what is the basic question we are asking?

What is the effect of
____?

Hypothesis:

Now, predict what you think will happen and tell why you made this prediction:

Procedure

1) Each lab group will be given either a Plant A or a Plant B, so that each partner group has a representation of each plant

2.) Remove a leaf that was covered in foil, and a leaf that was exposed. Remove the foil from the covered leaf, making sure to keep track of which leaf was which! Do you notice a difference in the area that was covered and the area that was exposed? Record your findings in the table below, and share your leaves and observations with your partner group:

Initial Plant A observations

Regular Leaf	Leaf Covered Partially in Foil

Initial Plant B observations

Regular Leaf	Leaf Covered Partially in Foil

3.) Once you have made your initial observations, your TA will assist you in prepping your leaves for the iodine test. The leaves will be boiled in 95% ethanol (alcohol) for about one minute.

4.) Place the leaves in separate petri dishes on your table. Add 5-6 drops of iodine to both sides of each leaf. You should add some to both sides, and hold the leaf by the stem to roll it around in the iodine until it is fully covered by the iodine. Let leaf react with the iodine for 4-5 minutes.

5.) Using the forceps, rinse the leaf in your beaker of water, then place it on a paper towel labeled A or B, based on which plant your leaf came from. Make note of the coloration pattern on each leaf, share information with your partner group, and record your observations in the tables:

Plant A observations after iodine

Regular Leaf	Leaf Covered Partially in Foil

Plant B observations after iodine

Regular Leaf	Leaf Covered Partially in Foil

CONCLUSION QUESTIONS

1. What was the independent variable in this experiment? What was the dependent variable? What were some of the controlled variables (constants)?

2. Why did we need to boil the leaves in alcohol before testing for starch (vs. the potato)?

3. What was the purpose of using one plant that had been exposed to light already and one that had not?

4. Summarize your results. Were your hypotheses correct? Which plant leaves tested positive for starch? Of those that did test positive, did they differ in coloration?

5. Relate your results to indications that photosynthesis was or was not occurring—explain. How does this relate to the equation?

Part III: Cellular Respiration Lab

Purpose:

To observe aerobic and anaerobic respiration of yeast in an enclosed environment, and to review the reactants and products of cellular respiration.

Background:

The yeast is a *facultative anaerobe*, meaning it will respire aerobically unless in an environment without oxygen, in which it will respire anaerobically. During anaerobic respiration, ATP molecules will be produced from glycolysis only. To continue the process of glycolysis, NAD+ (the electron carrier) needs regenerated. This occurs through the process of alcoholic fermentation, producing ethanol and carbon dioxide.

Question

What will happen if yeast is mixed with apple juice (sugar source) in a flask that is sealed with an empty balloon on top?

HYPOTHESIS

(Make a hypothesis before you start collecting any data other than baseline data. It should include information to back up your prediction.)

Procedure

- Place ½ teaspoon of yeast in an Erlenmeyer flask.
- Add 40 ml apple cider and mix.
- Cover the flask tightly with the balloon.
- Observe, fill in the chart, and make your hypothesis.
- Let sit for 20 minutes, and then make more measurements. Continue for an hour, checking and recording observations and measurements every 20 minutes.
- Graph the data using a best-fit line, and answer the questions.
    - For the graph, the independent variable goes on the X axis and the dependent variable goes on the Y axis. Make sure you label each axis with measurement AND unit. Do not connect the dots, but draw a straight best-fit line between the points. (Ask your instructor/GA to clarify.)

RESULTS

Table 1

Time	Circumference of Balloon (cm)	Observations of flask and balloon
Original		
20 minutes		
40 minutes		
60 minutes		

Figure 1 Balloon Circumference

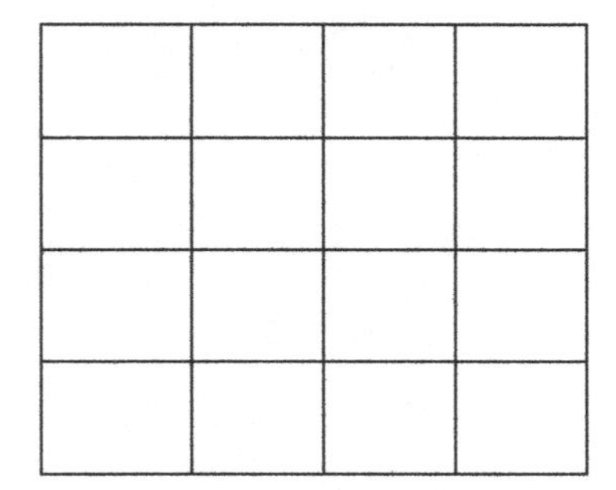

CONCLUSION QUESTIONS

1. Were the predictions of this experiment correct? Explain why or why not.

2. Describe the process(es) which caused the balloon to expand. Include the roles of the yeast and apple cider.

3. Will the balloon continue to expand indefinitely? Why or why not?

4. Could we perform the t-test or chi-squared test with this date? Explain.

6 FIELD ECOLOGY (by Janice Chism, Ph.D.)

Objectives

After completing this unit you will be able to:

- To develop an understanding of the structure of natural ecosystems
- To develop and test hypotheses about the way a natural community functions.
- To develop observational skills

Concepts covered in this lab:

Ecosystem	Climate	Developed Areas
Community	Primary Succession	Producers
Species	Secondary Succession	Consumers
Habitat	Climax community	Decomposers
Microhabitat	Woodland	Adaptation
Ecotone	Grassland	Competition
Biodiversity	Forest	

Introduction

This lab exercise is intended to introduce basic concepts in field ecology. Students will visit the Winthrop Woods Ecological Research and Instructional Area (here referred to as Winthrop Woods) for field instruction and they will carry out an investigation of some aspect of habitat structure and species diversity in the field. Students will give presentations on the results of their field projects at the end of the semester.

Winthrop Woods is an old field area. Originally the farm and dairy for Winthrop College, it produced most of the food consumed by Winthrop students up until about the mid-1950s. Since then parts of the farm have been allowed to revert to temperate deciduous forest. In our area oaks, hickories and maples dominate the forest with an understory of dogwoods and sweetgums. The process of reversion to the natural, *climax community* after some disturbance to a habitat is known as *secondary succession.*

As you walk around the Winthrop Woods area it will be obvious that it serves a variety of purposes. These include both formal and casual recreational use by the university and Rock Hill communities (for example, softball, soccer, jogging and dog walking) as well as instructional and research use by faculty and students. In addition, it is clear that the area has acquired importance as greenspace for the larger Rock Hill community as it experiences rapid growth and becomes increasingly urbanized.

As You Go Down in the Woods Today…
When you walk through the Winthrop Woods area, what do you see, hear, smell? Try to employ all of these senses, not just vision, in your "observations". Often a smell or sound will be just as important as something you see in the field. There are no areas of untouched, primary forest any more. You'll find a mix of natural and habitats created or maintained by humans. The main features of each major type of habitat are listed below but a major goal of this exercise is to help you develop your skills of observation. To do this we want you to get used to describing carefully and in detail what you observe using as many senses as possible.

Woodlands: These are (surprise, surprise) areas with trees. The trees can be of any type but they are fairly widely spaced so that their tops do not form a continuous canopy. In other words, when you stand in the middle of a woodland you can look up and see some open sky above you (if you aren't standing right under a large tree). Some classic examples of woodland habitats include the oak woodlands that cover the hillsides of much of coastal California (you can see this kind of habitat if you look at the countryside in the background of most car commercials), or acacia woodland in East Africa. Woodlands may or may not have a well-developed shrub layer near the ground.

Grasslands: These areas have few or no trees. They have ground cover predominantly of grasses, relatively short plants that usually have blades rather than leaves, inconspicuous flowers and belong to the family Graminae. But grasslands aren't made up only of grasses. If you walk through the grassland areas at the Woods and look carefully you will see that the "grass" actually includes many kinds of short plants, some of which may even have conspicuous or colorful flowers or interesting seeds (like dandelions). The plants that thrive in grasslands usually are pretty tolerant of sun and drought and of being trod upon. Grasslands may also have a few shrubs and vines growing in them. Some areas are permanent grasslands, like the prairies of the Midwestern U.S. or the classic savannas of Africa, while other grasslands are maintained as open areas because they are regularly disturbed by some feature such as fire or mowing. These "regularly-disturbed" grasslands do not represent *climax communities*. If left alone they would revert to woodland or forest via the process of *secondary succession*.

Forests: These are areas with many trees. In contrast to woodlands, forests usually have closed canopies. This means that if you stand in most parts of the forest and look up you will see the tops of trees with little visible sky. When you walk a way into a mature forest it is cool and shady and there isn't much in the way of a shrub layer. Depending on the forest type there may be vines or epiphytes (plants that grow on the trunks or limbs of trees with their roots hanging in the open air). A classic example of mature, primary forest of this type is the Amazonian rain forest, found in Brazil, Columbia, Ecuador and Peru in South America. Other examples include the temperate rain forest of the northwest Pacific coast, the redwood forests of Northern California and the oak-hickory forests of the Smokies and the Blue Ridge mountains of the southeastern U.S.

Winthrop Woods has no remaining old-growth primary forest but the second growth forest closely resembles the original forests in species composition if not in the size of the trees. Since this forest is in the southeast Piedmont, its natural climax community is a mix of deciduous trees dominated by oaks, hickories and maples. When a forest begins to regenerate it goes through a stage of succession in which conifers like red cedars and pines predominate. Later, deciduous trees, hardwoods like oaks and maples come in and take over. Some areas of our woods are about 25-30 years old. These areas are still at the cedar-pine stage of forest succession. Other areas are 60-70 years old and are dominated by hardwoods. A few trees remain that are even older than that, but long and extensive human use of this area has removed its ancient forests.

Successional Plots: These are three 50 X 50 meter areas that were established as demonstrations of the natural stages of succession from mowed field to early forest. The oldest of three plots was established in 1988, while the second plot was established in 1995 and the most recent in 2000. To establish a plot, the designated area is marked with stakes and the Winthrop grounds crew simply stops mowing it. Natural processes of succession do the rest. Gradually new plant and animal species invade the grassland and species that were there all along escape from the constant pruning of the mower and begin to grow. As the mix of species and the height profile of the plant cover changes, some species do better while others are out competed.

Developed Areas: It may seem strange to call a weedy field a “developed” area. If you think about what you’ve learned about succession and climax communities, however, you’ll immediately realize that a grassland or a soccer field only stays that way in this area by active human intervention – mowing, plowing or burning. If humans stop intervening, even briefly, the field returns to woods, eventually to forest. If you doubt this go out and look carefully at a lawn in any suburban area. You’ll probably see tiny little red cedars and pine trees coming up. If the owner of the lawn is conscientious about mowing, these baby trees will be constantly cut back and discouraged from growing. Their presence, however, is silent testimony to the power of succession. Stop mowing and the forest will return.

The Winthrop woods area has several kinds of developed areas. These include paved roads, buildings, the golf course you walked past, soccer and softball fields and mowed open areas. Despite all of this development and the relatively high level of human activity associated with it, the woods area has a fairly diverse resident animal and plant community.

The Animal Community: The Winthrop woods area contains a very diverse animal community including many species of birds, red foxes, rabbits, raccoons, possums, deer, skunks, feral cats, tree frogs, and several species of snakes.

Abiotic Components: Soil and water are important abiotic components of ecosystems. As you walk through the different habitats be sure to look at the soil and observe differences in color and texture. Water enters the Winthrop woods community as rain and via a seasonal stream that runs through the middle of the forest area.

Ecotones: These are areas where two or more types of habitats come together. Ecologists have found that these are particularly rich in species diversity – more so than the individual habitats themselves. The woods area has several *ecotones* between forest and grassland areas and between forest or grassland and human-maintained areas.

Thought Questions:

What factors determine whether or not a habitat has a well-developed shrub layer?

Why must grassland-adapted plants be sun and drought tolerant?

What kinds of animals do you think might make use of the grassland areas? What activities would these animals use this area for?

Do you think the grassland areas at Winthrop Woods represent a stable or climax stage of succession? Why? What factors might be acting to maintain these areas as grasslands?

Compare the evidence of animal activity you saw in the oldest successional plot? What about in the next oldest? The youngest? How would you explain any differences you observed in terms of differences in the physical structure and species composition of each habitat type?

What species of trees are most common in the woods nearest their interface with the path and grassland areas?

What kinds of trees do you see as you move deeper into the woods?

How could you use information about the species composition of different areas of the forest to figure out their relative ages?

In what part of the woods do you see more understory? What factors determine how much understory there is in a particular area?

In what part of the forest was the canopy most continuous? Would this be different if you visited the woods in winter then again in summer? Exlain why or why not? How is this related to the question about understory above?

List several specific examples of the following members of the community that you observed in the woods:

Producers

Primary Consumers

Secondary Consumers

Decomposers

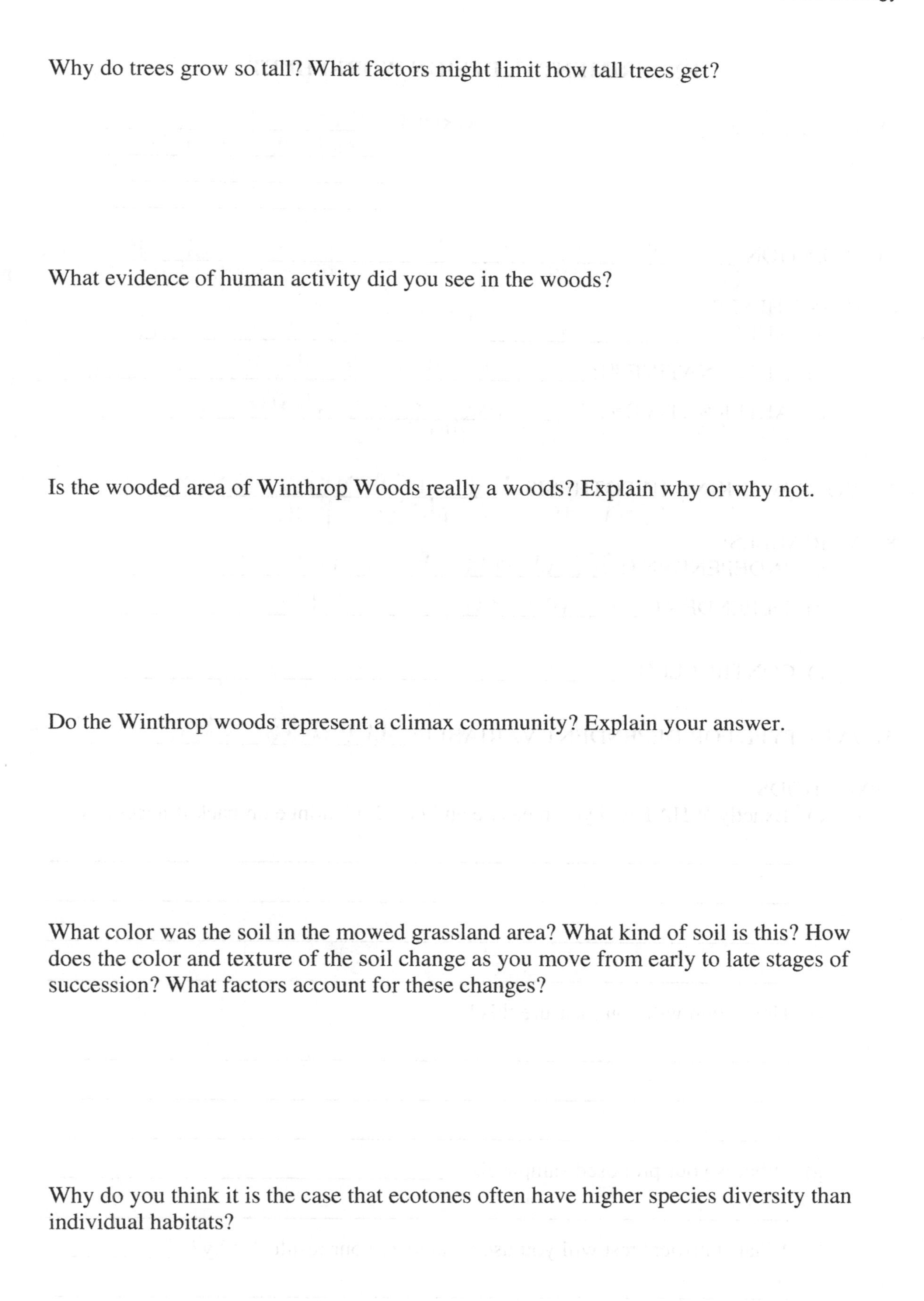

Why do trees grow so tall? What factors might limit how tall trees get?

What evidence of human activity did you see in the woods?

Is the wooded area of Winthrop Woods really a woods? Explain why or why not.

Do the Winthrop woods represent a climax community? Explain your answer.

What color was the soil in the mowed grassland area? What kind of soil is this? How does the color and texture of the soil change as you move from early to late stages of succession? What factors account for these changes?

Why do you think it is the case that ecotones often have higher species diversity than individual habitats?

EXPERIMENTAL DESIGN WORKSHEET

DATE 2-17-21 GROUP: Ainsley Lord
Gracie Martin

5) QUESTION: Is there a difference in the circumference of the trees in the oldest plot and the newest plot?

6) HYPOTHESES:
*circumference measured in cm

a) NULL: There is no difference in the circumferences.

b) ALTERNATIVE #1: The circumference of the trees will be greater in the newer plot.

c) ALTERNATIVE #2: The circumference of the trees will be greater in the older plot

7) YOUR WORKING HYPOTHESIS: The circumference of the trees will be greater in the oldest plot.

8) VARIABLES:

a) INDEPENDENT: age of ~~tree~~ (or plot)

b) DEPENDENT: circumference of trees

~~c)~~ CONTROLLED: ______

5) DATA TYPE FOR DEPENDENT VARIABLE: ~~continuous~~ continuous

6) METHODS:

e) Exactly WHAT will you measure and how? (Continue on back if necessary)

______

f) How often will you measure this?

______

g) What is your proposed sample size? ______

h) What statistical test will you use to analyze your results? Why? ______

Available Field Ecology Equipment

Plankton net-a net that you can use to concentrate and collect plankton from bodies of water by towing it across the water; samples are then observed under the microscope

Water Sampler- for collection of water samples at varying depths to measure DO, pH, nitrates etc.

Water Dipper-long handled apparatus to sample water in areas where it is hard to reach the water from the land

Berlese apparatus -used to extract arthropods from leaf litter or soil samples using heat from low watt incandescent light

Secchi disk- to measure the clarity and light penetration of pond and/or lake water.

pH waterproof tester-can be used in the field to test the pH of water samples

Dissolved oxygen meter-used to determine amount of dissolved oxygen in water samples

Portable soil pH meter-can be used in the field to test the pH of soil samples

Clinometer-for measuring the height of objects, such as trees

Light Meter- used to measure the density of light

Densitometer- can give you accurate estimates of canopy closure or vegetation cover

Insect Sieve

Tree calipers

Tape measures

Using Winthrop Farm (Woods, Lake and Wetland) for Research for Biology 151
Biology Department, Winthrop University

1. It is the intent of the Winthrop University Department of Biology to preserve Winthrop Farm in perpetuity as a variety of natural habitats for research and teaching purposes. The purpose of this request form is to makes sure that activities don't interfere with each other, and that, as much as possible, we can keep Facilities Management Informed so they won't damage our research projects or teaching objectives.

2. Students must complete a "Winthrop Farm Use Request Form" and have it signed by your instructor; it will then be submitted to Cassie Bell. This must happen BEFORE the project starts. We ask that students fill out a form, even if they are just making observations without setting out plots or traps.

3. If the activity involves only observations, you will be cleared to start your project within 24-48 hours.

4. Environmental impact of projects must be considered and approved before research can be started. If you are adding anything (exceptions are temporary markers), removing anything (including the organisms) or moving things around (examples included digging in the soil or moving leaf litter), you are manipulating the environment, which may have adverse effects. Janice Chism and Cassie Bell will meet to approve these type of proposals; students will be cleared as soon as possible to start their work (ideally within 24-48 hours also).

5. In cases of MAJOR manipulation, the chair of the Winthrop Farm Committee and the Committee will review the project. Approval would take as much as 1 to 2 weeks.

6. Projects to take place at the Wetlands will also be subject to approval of Jim Johnston and/or Dick Houk.

7. When your project is done, all materials used must be cleaned up and removed from the area, and it must be returned to its original state (or as close as possible).

Winthrop Farm Use Request Form for Biology 151 Students

Proposed research activity

Date____

Student name(s)____

151 Instructor____

Location of Winthrop Farm (wetland, woods, lake etc)____________________________

Species observed/ factor manipulated ____

Will plots be labeled or tagged in any way? ______________________________________

Describe the intent of your project/also discuss any proposed manipulations:

____ ________________

Student(s) signature(s) Date

____ ________________

151 Instructor signature (s) Date

____

Appropriate signature(s) of approval Date

7 HUMAN GENETICS

Objectives

After completing this unit you will be able to:

- demonstrate and describe how human traits are inherited
- produce and analyze human pedigrees
- explain how human genetic diseases are inherited
- understand the purpose of the Human Genome Project (HGP) and the usefulness of genetic databases
- debate public policy issues that pertain to the HGP

Introduction

The inheritance of human traits is of interest to us all. We carry the genes of our parents and of our grandparents, and when we reproduce, some of our traits will be passed on to our children. At family reunions, it is interesting to theorize where Johnny got his red hair or Jane her brown eyes.

A mistake, or mutation in the DNA sequence of a gene, can lead to a variation in the individual. Sometimes these variations are beneficial, but more often they produce an organism that can not survive or has a genetic disorder. Many genetic disorders are passed on from parent to offspring, and the presence of the defective gene can be traced through the use of **pedigrees** or family histories.

Scientists are currently in the process of sequencing the entire human genome in hopes of producing a data bank containing all the human genes. With this knowledge we will be able to pinpoint defects in a person's genetic makeup and possibly provide treatment for diseases that at this time are untreatable. What will be done with this knowledge, who will have access to it, and what will be considered a "normal" person are all issues that an informed public will need to address.

I. Inheritance of Human Genetic Characteristics

A. Genetic Variation

The reason related individuals often look different from each other is that they have different genotypes and, therefore, different phenotypes. This is true even for siblings who have the same parents. Only identical twins will not show these differences.

Inherited traits are expressed as phenotypes in different ways. A trait may show classic Mendelian dominant-recessive inheritance, incomplete dominance, or the trait may be controlled by more than one gene, a situation termed **polygenic**. But for every phenotype, there are only two genes, or alleles that a parent can pass on to offspring (Mendelian Law of Segregation). And for traits that are on different chromosomes, the inheritance of one trait does not depend on the inheritance of the other. (Mendelian law of Independent Assortment).

EXERCISE 14.1 Visualizing human genetic variation

To illustrate the tremendous variety possible in the human genome, you and a lab partner will produce the genotype and phenotype of a unique offspring. Which of the two alleles for a trait you pass on through your gametes is random and will be determined by flipping a coin. In order to simplify this procedure, **all parents are heterozygous for every trait.** You will record your offspring's genotype and then make a drawing to illustrate its phenotype.

1. With your lab partner, determine the gender of your baby. An individual who is XX is female and one who is XY is male. It is the father (XY) who determines the sex of a baby by contributing either an X or a Y chromosome to his offspring. A mother, whose genotype for gender is XX, will always contribute an X chromosome to her offspring. Have the "father" in your pair flip the coin to determine sex, heads = Y-chromosome and tails = X-chromosome.

2. On the data sheet (*Table 14.1*) fill in your names and the gender of your baby. Also choose a name for your child and record the name.

3. Determine each of your offspring's 15 other inherited traits, using the pictures below. **Each** parent now flips the coin to determine which form of each of their genes will go to the baby. Remember that **parents are heterozygous for all traits.** Heads always represents the dominant or uppercase allele; tails represents the recessive or lower case allele. For traits that show incomplete dominance, a heterozygous individual will be a new phenotype.

Inherited Traits.

A. Mendelian Dominant/Recessive Inheritance

1. Widow's Peak: Parents are both Ww

Present (WW,Ww) Absent (ww)

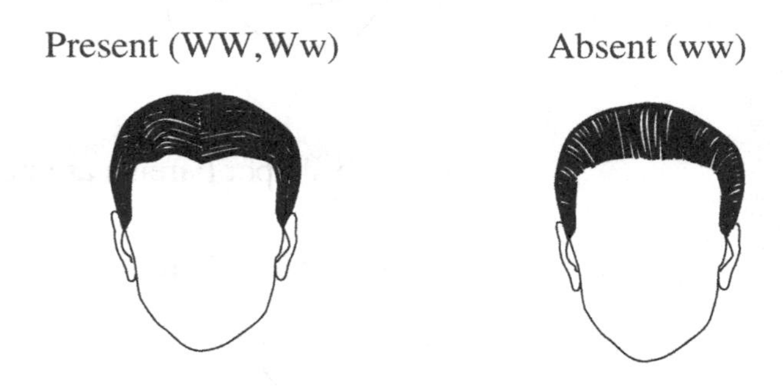

2. Eyebrows: Parents are both Bb

Bushy (BB, Bb) Fine (bb)

3. Eyelashes: Parents are both Ll

Long (LL, Ll) Short (ll)

4. Lips: Parents are both Tt

Thick (TT, Tt)

Thin (tt)

5. Dimples: Parents are both Dd

Dimples (DD, Dd)

No dimples (dd)

6. Nose shape: Parents are both Rr

Rounded (RR, Rr)

Pointed (rr)

7. Freckles on cheeks: Parents are both Ff

Freckles (FF, Ff)

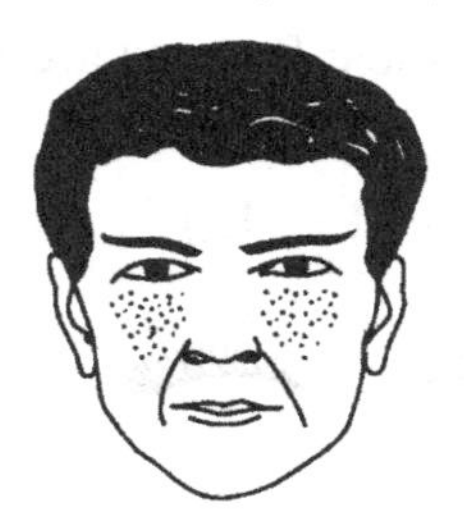

No freckles (ff)

8. Face shape: Parents are both Rr

Rounded (Rr, Rr) Squarish (rr)

9. Earlobe attachment: Parents are both Ff

Free (FF, Ff) Attached (ff)

B. Incomplete Dominance

1. Hair Type: Parents are both Cc

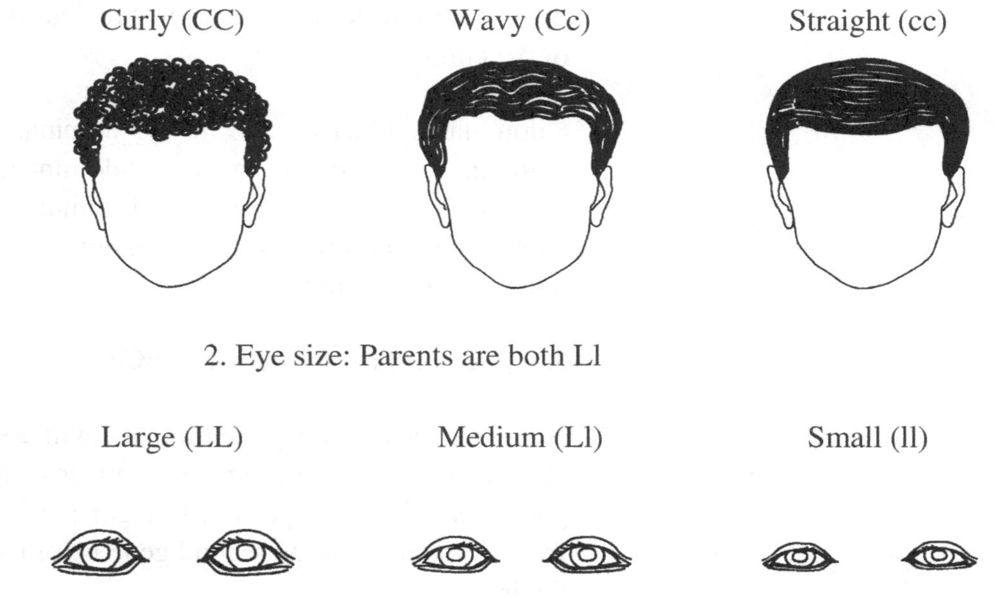

2. Eye size: Parents are both Ll

3. Mouth length: Parents are both Ll

Long (LL) Average (Ll) Short (ll)

4. Nose size: Parents are both Ll

Large (LL) Medium (Ll) Small (ll)

C. Polygenic Inheritance

1. Hair Color: Parents are both AaBbCcDd

Hair color is produced by several different pairs of alleles (a polygenic trait). There are four pairs of alleles involved. Thus it will take four tosses of the coins to determine the genotype of the child.

8 dominants = black
7 dominants = very dark brown
6 dominants = dark brown
5 dominants = brown
4 dominants = light brown
3 dominants = dark blonde
2 dominants = blonde
1 dominant = light blonde
0 dominants = almost white

2. Eye color: Parents are both BbCc

Again we have a polygenic trait. We will assume two pairs of alleles and therefore each parent must toss the coin twice to get the baby's genotype. The first gene is for the pigment in front of the iris and the second gene is for the pigment behind the iris.

BBCC = dark brown	BBCc = dark brown
BbCC = brown w/ green flecks	BBcc = brown
BbCc = brown	Bbcc = blue-gray
bbCC = green	bbCc = dark blue
bbcc = light blue	

4. For each trait, record in *Table 14.1* the genes donated by the mother, the genes donated by the father, and the resulting genotype of the baby. Also describe how the trait will appear in the baby (phenotype).

Parent's Names: Ainsley Lord and Gracie Martin

Child's Name Big Stuff Child's Sex Male (heads=boy; tails=girl)

#	Trait	Allele from Mother	Allele from Father	Baby's Genotype	Baby's Phenotype
1.	Widow's peak	W	W	WW	WIDOWS PEAK
2.	Eyebrows	B	b	Bb	BUSHY
3.	Eyelashes	l	l	ll	SHORT
4.	Lips	t	t	tt	THIN
5.	Dimples	D	D	DD	DIMPLES
6.	Nose shape	R	r	Rr	ROUNDED
7.	Freckles	f	F	Ff	FRECKLES
8.	Face shape	R	R	RR	ROUNDED
9.	Earlobe Attachment	f	f	ff	ATTACHED
10.	Hair type	C	C	CC	CURLY
11.	Eye size	l	l	ll	SMALL
12.	Mouth length	L	l	Ll	AVG
13.	Nose size	l	l	ll	SMALL
14.	Hair color				BLONDE
15.	Eye color	Bc	bc	Bbcc	BLUE-GRAY

Table 14.1 Data on hypothetical baby

5. When you have determined all 15 traits for your baby. Use the paper and crayons provided to draw a picture of your baby. Be sure to include your baby's name.

6. Display your drawing in the front of the class.

7. Analyze one dominance controlled trait, eyebrows, to determine if its inheritance follows Mendelian predictions.

Since the entire class consists of identical "parents", we can consider every baby as coming from the same set of parents. A large sample size will increase the chances that hair type will follow Mendel's 3:1 ratio for a heterozygous cross showing dominance.

Total number of babies in sample: ____________

- How are these "babies" related to one another?

	# with trait	**ratio**
dominant phenotype for eyebrows __________	__________	_________
recessive phenotype for eyebrows __________	__________	_________

- Does your actual ratio of eyebrow types match the predicted ratio? Why or why not?

B. Human Genetic Analysis

Inheritance of specific traits in humans is not as easy to follow as inheritance of traits in pea plants or fruit flies. Humans have a much longer life span and produce fewer offspring than the organisms geneticists generally use for laboratory studies. Inheritance of specific human traits is very important to each of us as individuals. Particularly important is the inheritance of altered genes that are expressed as a genetic disease. Geneticists often put together pedigrees to analyze human inheritance. A pedigree is a chart used to show the genetic connections between generations. If enough data is available, geneticists can sometimes predict what a child will inherit from his/her parents.

EXERCISE 14.2 Pedigree development

A series of boxes and ovals connected by lines can be used to visualize family relationships. A box represents the male, an oval a female. Lines connect a couple that have produced a child, and show the connection between one generation and the next.

1. *Figure 14.1* below models the inheritance of earlobe attachment. Free earlobes dominate attached lobes. The F_1 individuals genotypes are listed. Draw in the appearance of their ears.

2. The offspring these two parents could produce are shown in the F_2 generation. Draw in their phenotypes on *Figure 14.1* below.

3. A pedigree can also be used to trace previous generations. Draw the possible parents (P_1) phenotypes in *Figure 14.1.*

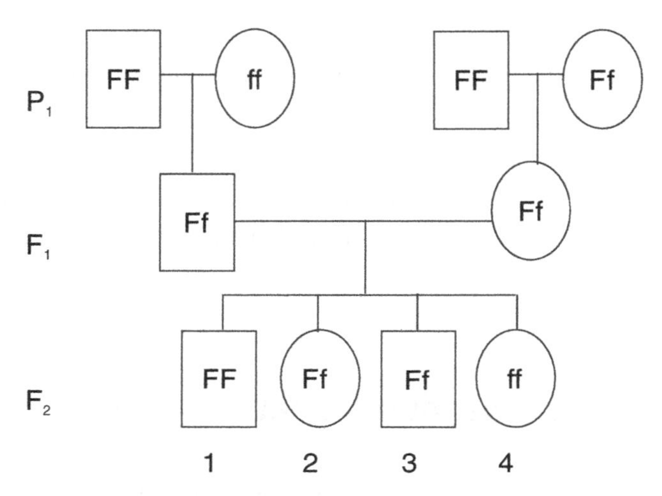

Figure 14.1 Pedigree of ear attachment

EXERCISE 14.3 Autosomal inheritance

Human cells contain 23 pairs of chromosomes in their nuclei. One pair of chromosomes, the **sex chromosomes** which are designated with an X or a Y, contain the genes that deal with gender. The other 22 pairs of chromosomes, termed **autosomes**, code for other traits besides gender. Many autosomal genetic disorders require the individual to have two copies of a defective gene in order to be affected by the disorder. Individuals with one defective copy (heterozygous) are said to be **carriers**. A carrier can pass the affected gene to their offspring, but the individual will show no effects of the defective gene because they have one normal gene that produces enough product for normal physiological functions. An example of an autosomal recessive disorder is **sickle-cell**

anemia, a genetic disorder which produces abnormal hemoglobin in red blood cells. A person afflicted with sickle cell anemia produces red blood cells that are sickle-shaped and tend to rupture and clog capillaries. This causes extreme pain and can cause severe tissue and organ damage. Other autosomal recessive disorders include **albinism** (absence of skin pigmentation) and **phenylketonuria (PKU)** where a missing enzyme leads to the buildup of phenylalanine which can in turn lead to mental retardation. **Galactosemia** is also caused by a defective gene failing to produce an enzyme necessary in the breakdown of milk. Untreated, galactosemia can lead to brain, liver and eye damage.

1. In this exercise you will predict the "reproductive" outcome of two F1 individuals who are carriers for sickle-cell anemia. These individuals have one normal gene (N) and one defective gene (n).

2. Predict the types of offspring these two parents can produce and list the genotypes of these offspring in Figure 14.2 in the F2 generation.

3. Two of the parents of the F1 individuals have genotypes that are shown in *Figure 14.2*. Predict and fill in the ovals for the other parent's possible genotypes.

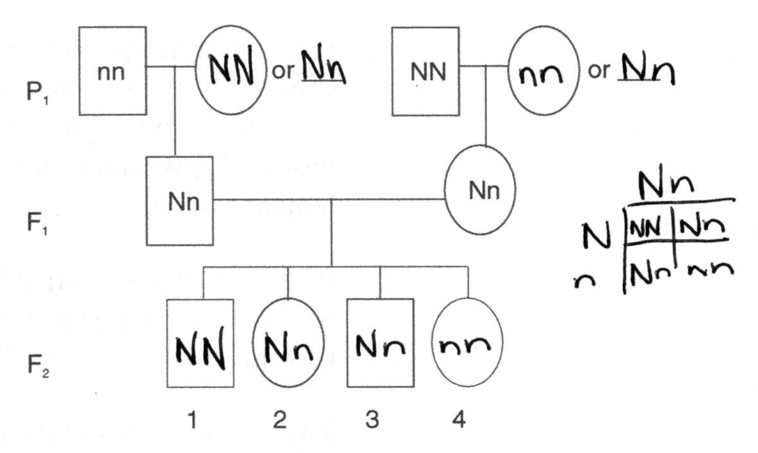

Figure 14.2 Human pedigree, sickle-cell anemia inheritance

- What are the parental genotypes of the F1 generation? Phenotypes?

- What percentage of F1 individuals are normal? Are carriers?

- What percentage of F_2 individuals are normal? Are carriers? Are affected?
- Describe the symptoms of the genetic disorder you modeled.

EXERCISE 14.4 X-linked inheritance

The sex chromosomes are different from autosomes in that the X and Y genes do not code for the same traits, even though they pair during meiosis. The X chromosome is larger than the Y chromosome and codes for many traits unrelated to gender.

Certain genetic diseases, termed X-Linked, are caused by a defect in a gene found on the X chromosome. Males, who only inherit one X chromosome, are much more likely to express the phenotype of X-Linked disorders than females, who inherit two X chromosomes. Examples of X-Linked recessive inheritance include **Duchenne muscular dystrophy (DMD)**, a muscle wasting disease. Hemophilia A, a blood-clotting disorder, linked to the x chromosome results from a defective gene. Queen Victoria of England was a carrier and passed this gene to several of her children (see lab question #4). **Red-green color blindness** results in persons who can not distinguish red from green in dim light.

1. In this exercise you will predict the outcome of a cross between two individuals, a color blind man (X^nY) and his wife (X^NX^n) who is a carrier for color blindness. Normal color vision (X^N) is dominant over different forms of color blindness (X^n).

2. Predict the types of offspring these two parents can produce and list the genotypes of these offspring in *Figure 14.3* in the F_2 generation.

3. Two of the parents of the F_1 individuals have genotypes that are shown in *Figure 14.3*. Predict and fill in the other parent's genotype.

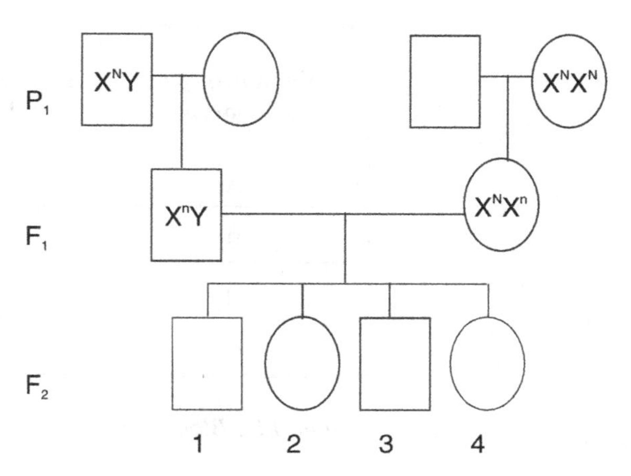

Figure 14.3 Human pedigree, color blindness inheritance

- What are the parental genotypes of the F1 generation? Phenotypes?
- What percentage of F1 individuals are affected? Are carriers?
- What percentage of F2 individuals are normal? Are carriers? Are affected?
- Describe the symptoms of the genetic disorder you modeled.

C. Inheritance of Blood Groups

Many human traits are determined by **multiple alleles**. Where there are more than two possible alleles, any of these alleles can occupy a locus. Human blood types are determined by three alleles termed I^A, I^B, and i. The alleles I^A and I^B code for production of two proteins, antigen A or antigen B, on the surface of red blood cells. Alleles I^A and I^B are **codominant.** If a person inherits these two alleles, both protein types will be expressed on their red blood cells. The **i** allele is recessive.

Each human belongs to one of the four ABO blood phenotypes and one of the six ABO genotypes. *Table 14.2* lists both groupings. By convention, we use the letter I to represent a blood allele.

Blood group or phenotype	Type of antigen on red blood cell	Genotypes	
A	A	I^AI^A	I^Ai
B	B	I^BI^B	I^Bi
AB	A and B	I^AI^B	
O	(None)	ii	

Table 14.2 Blood groups

EXERCISE 14.5 Inheritance of blood groups

- Is it possible for a child of blood type AB to be produced by two type O parents? _______ Explain.

- In a case of disputed paternity, the child is type O, the mother is type B.
  Mother's genotype _______
  Child's genotype _______

- Which individuals of the following blood types could be the father?

  O ______
  A ______
  B ______
  AB ______

EXERCISE 14.6 Blood type problems

Cross #1

A person heterozygous for type A blood marries someone who is heterozygous for type B blood. List the types of offspring they could have and the probability for each blood type in the offspring.

Cross #2

For this problem, use the information given in the previous problem. A woman with type O blood gave birth to a baby with type O blood. In a court case she claims that a certain man is the father of her child. The man has type A blood.

- Could he be the father?
- Does this evidence alone prove that he is the father?

II. Bioethics and the Human Genome Project

The human genome project (HGP) is a coordinated effort by scientists from around the world to record the complete sequence of the human genome, as well as the genomes of other research organisms. A **genome** is the complete complement of an organism's genes or genetic material. To record the human DNA sequences will require the equivalent of 200 telephone books of 1000 pages each. The data analysis and storage requirements of the HGP are such that **electronic databases** have been developed to speed up analysis of the DNA sequences, as well as to streamline the storage and retrieval of the data.

HGP-related research has already produced significant information about the human genome. For example, scientists have recently described a new autosomal dominant disease mechanism that involves the expansion of short segments of DNA to many times their normal length. There are at least six human disorders that are a result of expanded DNA segments, and all of them produce defects in nervous system functions. **Huntington disease** and **fragile X** are two of the disorders that are caused by multiple repeats of DNA segments.

Many individuals are concerned that information generated by the genomic research may have ethical and legal implications that society is not prepared to face. Health care workers will have to deal with complicated scientific and clinical questions their patients might have regarding the results of genetic tests. Likewise, each of us as individuals will have to make personal decisions as to our life style, marriage and offspring in relation to our genetic makeup.

A. Genetic Screening

As the genes which cause specific genetic disorders have been pinpointed, scientists have developed tests to screen individuals for these particular disorders. An individual will contribute body cells, found either in a blood sample or from a swab of cheek epithelial cells. From these cells, an individual's DNA can be isolated and analyzed.

EXERCISE 14.7 Individual genetic screening

1. A series of imaginary people have contributed cheek cells to be analyzed by a science lab for the presence of genetic abnormalities. The DNA of these fictitious people was analyzed for the following disorders:

Type of Inheritance	Disorder	Description of Symptoms	Positive Test Color
Autosomal Recessive	Sickle-cell Anemia		red
	Phenylketonuria		blue
Autosomal Dominant	Huntington's disorder		green
X-Linked Recessive	Duchenne muscular dystrophy		yellow
	Hemophilia A		black

Table 14.3 Human genetic disorders

In the table above, fill in a description of the symptoms for each disorder.

2. Obtain an envelope containing the results of a fictitious person's genetic screening. The envelope contains swabs of cheek cells which were used to screen for the genetic disorders described in #1.

3. Before opening your envelope, you and your peers must discuss and come to a consensus as to how this information should be handled.

   There are four possible options you may choose:

   Option 1 - report the results of the tests anonymously
   Option 2 - report the results individually only to the person tested
   Option 3 - enter individual's results into a regulated genetic data base
   Option 4 - report individual's results openly

4. Your instructor will write these options on the board, and then list the student's viewpoints. Fill in the student viewpoints under the options below:

Option 1 - **Report only the anonymous results of the tests**

reasons to report anonymously	reasons not to report anonymously

Option 2 - **Report individual's results only to the person tested**

reasons to report to individual	reasons not to report to individual

Option 3 - **Enter individual's results into a regulated genetic data base**

reasons to use a regulated data base	reasons not to use a regulated data base

Option 4 - **Report individual's results openly**

reasons to report openly	reasons not to report openly

4. Vote as a class for one of the above options. Your instructor will provide you with additional information according to which of the above options your class chose.

5. If you are to open the envelope and determine the results of your individual's genetic tests, do so now. Look inside the envelope and determine the color of the tips of each swab. **Do not remove the swabs from the envelope.** Use *Table 14.3* to determine the results of each test.

- Which option did your class choose?
- What information did you obtain about the genetic tests?
- What (if any) information is still confidential?

B. Public Policy Development

An informed public will be responsible for deciding how genetic information should be used. Every individual in our society has a right to privacy guaranteed by the constitution and the right to make individual choices. The data made available through genetic tests, however, can be used to benefit mankind as a whole. In the following exercise you will discuss ethical concepts related to genetic databases and decide what public policy you would endorse.

Case Study

Lisa is a six-year old girl who was diagnosed as having phenylketonuria (PKU) at two weeks of age. A low phenylalanine diet was prescribed at the time of diagnosis. Routine assessments done at the age of one month, one year and two years revealed normal development for her age. Through proper diet, Lisa's growth and development have been normal. Lisa continues to be heathy today.

Recently, Lisa's father changed jobs and the new health insurance provider notified the family that, because of Lisa's early diagnosis, she was considered high risk and ineligible for insurance coverage under their group plan. Lisa's parents investigated and discovered that the new insurance company, as a matter of operating procedure, sends information concerning all new clients to Consolidated Information Systems, Inc (CIS). This company stores medical, life, and disability insurance information in a registry that is available to insurance companies for a fee. A check on the new employee and his family revealed Lisa's earlier diagnosis and denied coverage for Lisa.

Lisa's medical expenses are currently paid by the family. The family has appealed to the agency that administers the group insurance plan, the chairman of the corporation Lisa's father works for, and also the state insurance commissioner.

EXERCISE 14.8 Public policy development

1. Form a group with the students at your lab table. Elect a chairperson to guide the discussion and present your arguments to the class.

2. Read the above case study and discuss phenylketonuria (PKU).

3. Each group will be assigned one of the following recommendations:

   Recommendation A:
   There should be no *new* laws developed until more is known about the use of genetic information found in databases.

   Recommendation B:
   New laws should be written that guarantee an individual's right to privacy with respect to genetic information found in databases.

   Recommendation C:
   New laws should be written that limit an individual's right to privacy if releasing the genetic information found in databases can be shown to be in the best interests either of that individual or of the community as a whole.

4. Each group will discuss their assigned recommendation and focus on how their policies would work in the PKU case study.

Arguments for Recommendation:

5. Ask your chairperson to present the arguments for your recommendation to the class. Discuss and record the pros and cons of each recommendation.

   Recommendation A: ______________________________

   Reasons this recommendation should be chosen:

   Reasons this recommendation should *not* be chosen:

   Recommendation B: ______________________________

   Reasons this recommendation should be chosen:

   Reasons this recommendation should *not* be chosen.

Recommendation C: ______________________________

Reasons this recommendation should be chosen:

Reasons this recommendation should *not* be chosen:

6. Vote for the policy you would personally like to see implemented. You *do not* have to vote in agreement with what your group recommended.

- What was the result of your class vote?

- Consider the PKU case. Would the recommendation your class chose benefit Lisa and her family? How?

-

-

- Would the recommendation your class chose benefit the insurance company in the PKU case? How?

Summary Questions

1. Give examples of human traits that show these patterns of inheritance:
   dominant/recessive
   incomplete dominance
   polygenic inheritance
   codominance

2. What are some advantages of laws that place strict protections on the privacy of genetic information? What are some disadvantages of such laws?

3. What is a genetic database and why is it useful? How could it be harmful?

4. Queen Victoria of England was a carrier of the genetic disorder which causes hemophilia A. The following diagram is a partial pedigree of her family.

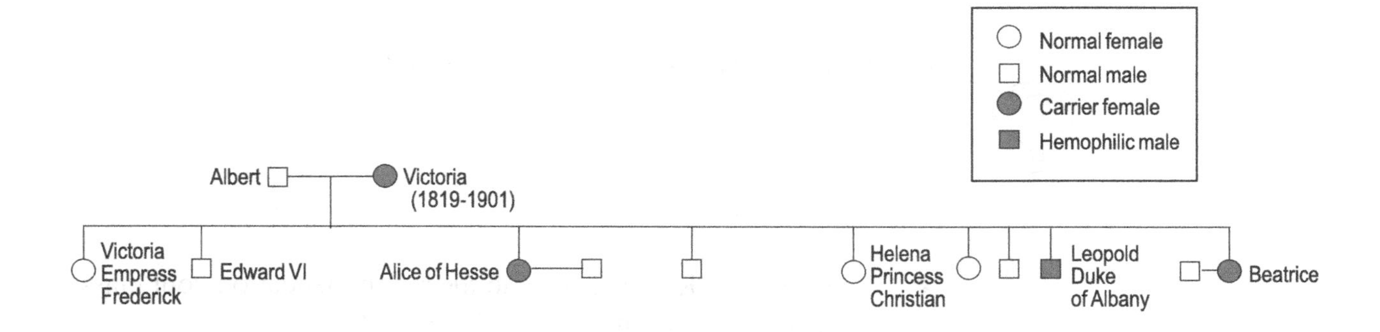

- How many sons did Queen Victoria have?
- Of her sons, what percentage were hemophiliacs?
- What percentage of her daughters were carriers of the hemophilia gene?
- Overall, who does hemophilia affect more, males or females?

8 MOLECULAR GENETICS Modeling DNA and RNA

(by Cassandra Bell, M.S.)

Background information

- DNA stands for <u>D</u>eoxyribo<u>N</u>ucleic <u>A</u>cid. It is a long thin molecule that controls the reproduction, development and functioning of living things.
- It contains an organism's complete collection of genetic info *(its genome)* packaged in units called **genes**.
- Genes "code" for the production of **proteins** that will do most of the work of the cell.
- Each descendent of a cell <u>must</u> have DNA to survive.

Structure of DNA

- To describe the structure of a DNA molecule, we often use the analogy of an *open, spiral staircase* in which the "handrails" are a repeating series of **sugar (deoxyribose)** and **phosphate molecules**, while the "steps" are a pair of **nitrogen bases.**
- The nitrogen bases are **A=adenine, C=cytosine, G=guanine, and T=thymine** (*A always pairs with T, and C with G; these pairs are held together by a hydrogen bond*).
- A **nucleotide** of DNA consists of a phosphate, a deoxyribose sugar and one of the four bases. One DNA molecule consists of billions of nucleotides.
- The **order of the nitrogen bases** in a DNA molecule is extremely varied. The order of the nitrogen bases within different segments of the DNA molecule (genes) **codes for proteins** needed by that particular living thing.

ACTIVITY #1- Building a DNA model

To better understand the composition and function of a DNA molecule, construct a model using the following code.

- **PHOSPHATE= white tubes**
- **DEOXYRIBOSE SUGARS= black pentagons**
- **NITROGEN BASES=**
  - **Cytosine (C)= blue tubes**
  - **Thymine (T) = green tubes**
  - **Adenine (A)= orange tubes**
  - **Guanine (G) = yellow tubes**
- **HYDROGEN BONDS= white rods**

1. Build 12 **nucleotides**. (3 with cytosine , 3 with guanine, 3 with adenine, and 3 with thymine). REMEMBER, each nucleotide has 1 base, 1 phosphate, and 1 sugar.
2. Use these nucleotides to construct your model; it should be 6 "steps". Always pair G with C and T with A using the hydrogen bonds to connect them. You may choose the sequence of the bases, but try to have at least one of each base on both sides of your ladder. Remember the sugar and phosphate will always alternate.
3. Show your teacher your finished model.
4. Keep this model for the next activity.

NOTE: In reality, a DNA molecule is BILLIONS of base pairs (or "steps") long!!!

ACTIVITY #2- DNA Replication

- Remember, for cell division to occur, the DNA must first be replicated.
- *HOW DOES IT HAPPEN???*
- Basically, the original DNA molecule splits down the middle, and then, a new molecule comes about via nitrogen base pairing.

Follow these steps to model DNA replication.

1. Build 12 more nucleotides of DNA (same as step #1 in activity 1), but do not make a second molecule.
2. Split or "unzip" your DNA model down the middle by separating the nitrogen base pairs at the hydrogen bonds (these are weak bonds).
3. Bring in the new nucleotides built in step one of this activity and pair them up to the two sides of the unzipped molecule.
4. When finished, you should have two identical DNA molecules. Check to be sure they are identical. (Each molecule is now half the original DNA model and half the new DNA).
5. Keep one model together for the next activity, and set the other one aside for spare parts.

ACTIVITY #3-PROTEIN PRODUCTION PART I- Modeling Transcription

- Remember, **proteins** do most of the work of the cell.
- The DNA molecule codes for the production of these proteins. There are two steps.
- We will first model transcription; this is when the needed genetic information encoded in the DNA is copied onto *messenger RNA* (**mRNA**).
- ***WHAT IS RNA?*** (ribonucleic acid)
- Similar to DNA as it has the alternating sugar and phosphate "handrail" joined to nitrogen bases

- <u>Different from DNA</u> as usually single-stranded, the sugar is **ribose**, and the nitrogen base **uracil** (U) replaces thymine (T). Uracil will bond with adenine.

<u>Code for additional parts</u>
URACIL (U)= purple tube
RIBOSE SUGAR= purple pentagon

1. Unzip the DNA model, and choose one side to be the one that will be transcribed by the messenger RNA.
2. Construct 6 mRNA nucleotides which can pair with the DNA to be transcribed.
3. Bond the mRNA nucleotides with their matching DNA nitrogen bases.
4. Unzip the mRNA at the hydrogen bonds. The original DNA molecule joins back together again.

AFTER YOU ANSWER #1 FOR ACTIVITY #4, PUT YOUR MODEL PARTS AWAY, AND CONTINUE DOWN THE PATH OF PROTEIN PRODUCTION VIA PAPER AND PENCIL.

Activity # 4 – PROTEIN PRODUCTION PART II- Translation

- Now that the mRNA transcript is formed, it will leave the nucleus of the cell *(the DNA cannot leave the nucleus)* and go to the ribosome to put together the protein; this step is translation.
- Every 3 bases in the mRNA is a **codon**, and it codes for either an **amino acid** or to start or stop. (See tables and figures provided in your textbook and by your instructor.)
- The **amino acids** will be put together to form proteins
- **<u>Transfer RNA (tRNA)</u>** : molecule that brings the amino acids to the ribosomes and match up by pairing their bases with the mRNA; this is the **anti-codon**.

1. Write down your two codons (two triplets) from your mRNA transcript.

   _______ _______ ________ ***** ______ _______ _______

2. What would be the corresponding match for the tRNA (anti-codon) that will attach to the mRNA ?

   _______ _______ ________ ***** ______ _______ _______

3. Use tables and figures provided to decipher which amino acids the tRNA will bring to the ribosome. Hint: refer to the original codons (not the anticodons).

4. ___________***** ____________*****= polypeptide chains which bond together the amino acids to form the protein.

NOTE: IT USUALLY TAKES HUNDREDS OF AMINO ACIDS TO FORM A PROTEIN.

MORE PRACTICE/CHECK FOR UNDERSTANDING:

1. If the nitrogen bases of one side of a DNA molecule are ATT CAG GGC TCA, what is the matching side?

2. Protein production from start to finish.
Fill in the chart.

DNA	TAC	CCT	GAC	ATT
MRNA (codon)				
tRNA (anticodon)				
Amino acid code				
Amino acid				

3. Compare and contrast DNA and RNA.

4. If a DNA analysis shows 30% adenine bases, what would be the percentage of thymine?_____ cytosine?_______ guanine?_________ and uracil?__________

5. In your words, describe the steps of DNA replication, and tell why it occurs.

6. Describe the steps of protein production (transcription and translation), and tell why it occurs.

7. List from smallest to biggest:nucleotide, chromosome, cell, nitrogen base, nucleus, mRNA

8. What will be the effect of a DNA mutation that changes a portion of the DNA which used to say CTC to CAC? What if it changes from CTC to CTT?

9 THE CELL

Objectives

After completing this unit you will be able to:

- explain how the development of the microscope contributed to the development of the cell theory
- describe the similarities and differences between prokaryotic and eukaryotic cells
- identify each cell part and state its function
- distinguish between plant and animal cells

Introduction

In the 17th century Robert Hooke built a microscope powerful enough to see objects at greater magnifications than had previously been possible. Hooke used his new microscope to examine many things—minerals, cloth, small plants, and small animals. After examining a thin piece of cork, he observed many individual units making up the cork. He published a report in 1665 in which he called these units cells because they reminded him of the small cubicles that monks lived in.

Other scientists began to use microscopes to examine the tissues of animals and plants and often saw structures that reminded them of the cork cells Hooke had described. Over the next 150 years, scientists realized that all living things are composed of cells. This laboratory session will give you an opportunity to examine cells and help you appreciate why an understanding of this basic unit of life is so important.

I. Cell Theory

With better microscopes, scientists were able to make accurate observations of cells and gradually the **cell theory** developed. Currently this theory has three parts:

- all organisms are composed of one or more cells
- the cell is the basic *living* unit of organization
- all cells arise from pre-existing cells

Improved microscopes enabled scientists to better observe cell organization, size, and function. All cells have the following structures:

- a **plasma membrane** defining the boundary of the living material
- a region of **DNA (deoxyribonucleic acid),** which stores genetic information
- a **cytoplasm** including everything inside the plasma membrane that is not part of the DNA region

There are two basic types of cells: **eukaryotic**, those with a clearly defined nucleus and cell organelles, and **prokaryotic**, those without these structures. The Greek word **karyon** means kernel, referring to the nucleus. Thus, **prokaryotic** means "before a nucleus," while **eukaryotic** means "true nucleus" indicating the presence of a nucleus. Examine *Table 6.1* and identify the differences between prokaryotic and eukaryotic cells.

Prokaryotic cells, typical of modern bacteria and cyanobacteria, are believed to be similar to the first cells that developed on earth billions of years ago. Eukaryotic cells have probably evolved from prokaryotes.

Characteristics	Prokaryotic Cells	Eukaryotic Cells
Genetic material	Located in **nucleoid**, a region of cytoplasm not bounded by a membrane. Consists of a single molecule of DNA. Plasmid, a single small loop of DNA separate from the nucleoid.	Located in a **nucleus**, a membrane-bound compartment within the cytoplasm. Made up of DNA molecules with proteins. Organized into chromosomes.
Cytoplasm	Small ribosomes. Photosynthetic membranes arising from the plasma membrane in some species.	Large ribosomes. Organelles, membrane-bounded compartments which perform specific cell functions.

Table 6.1 Characteristics of prokaryotic and eukaryotic cells

II. Prokaryotic Cells

EXERCISE 6.1 Observe bacteria cells

1. Under the dissecting microscope, observe the culture plate containing bacteria growing on a nutrient media. The dots you see are masses of bacterial cells called colonies, each originating from one cell that has divided many times.

2. Under the compound light microscope and using a prepared slide, observe the microscopic structure of bacterial cells. The slide is a preparation of stained individual bacterial cells.

- What magnification is needed to view the bacteria? _______X
- Can you see organelles within the cytoplasm?

3. Draw the bacteria cells and record the magnification (*Figure 6.1*).

4. Measure the approximate size (µm) of the bacteria cells. Refer to the microscope unit if you have forgotten how to estimate the size of microscopic structures.

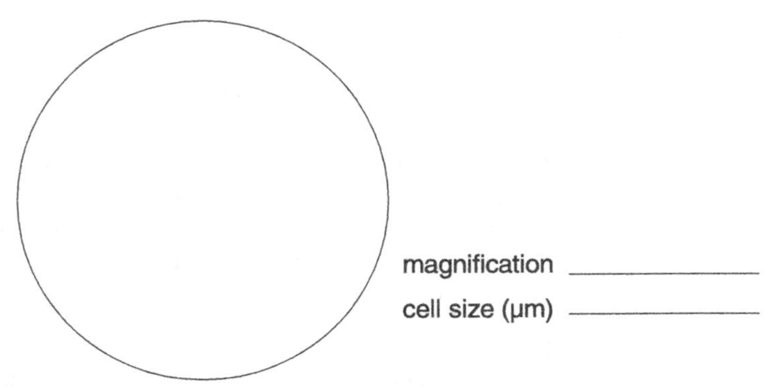

Figure 6.1 Drawing of prokaryotic cells

5. Examine the drawing of the bacterium (*Figure 6.2*). The cell has a **cell wall,** a structure different from the wall of plant cells but serving the same primary function. The **plasma membrane** is flat against the cell wall and may be difficult to see. Look for two components in the **cytoplasm:** the small black dots called **ribosomes** which give the cytoplasm its granular appearance; the **nucleoid**, a relatively electron-transparent region (appears light) containing fine threads of DNA.

6. Label the structures of the bacterial cell (*Figure 6.2*).

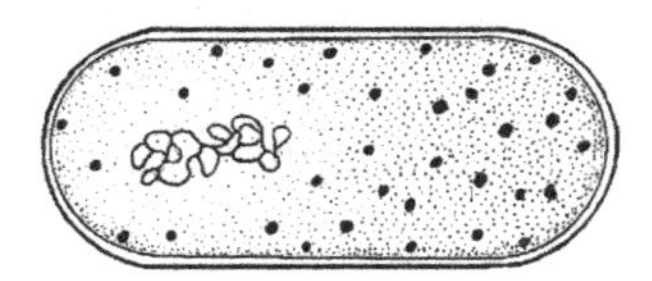

Figure 6.2 A bacterial cell

III. Eukaryotic Cells

A. Animal Cells

EXERCISE 6.2 Prepare a wet mount of human cheek cells

1. Use a clean toothpick and gently scrape the inside of your cheek with the flattened end of the toothpick.

2. Stir the scrapings into a drop of water on a clean microscope slide and add a coverslip.

3. Methylene blue is a dye that will stain the cell's nucleus darker than the cytoplasm. Stain your sample by adding a drop of stain to one side of the coverslip and touching a piece of absorbent paper to the opposite side of the coverslip (*Figure 6.3*). Do not remove the coverslip.

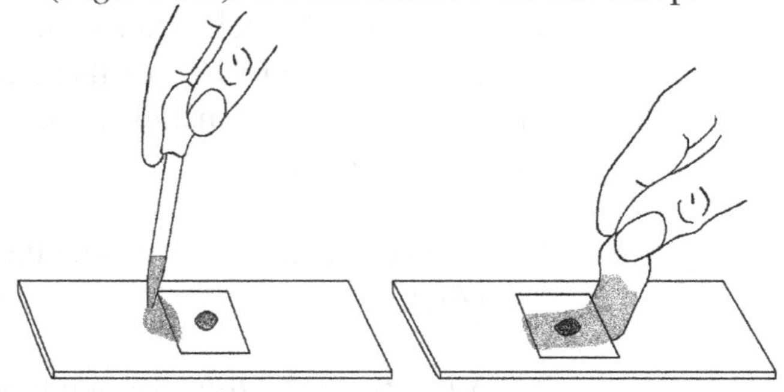

Figure 6.3 Technique for staining specimen

4. Locate the cheek cells using low power, then switch to high power for a more detailed view. Find the **nucleus**, a round centrally located body within each cell.

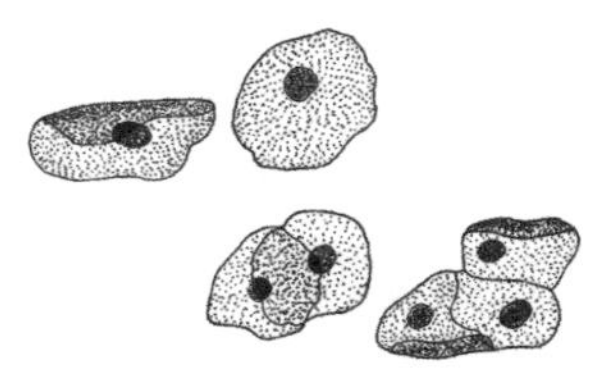

Figure 6.4 Human cheek cells

5. Carefully draw several cheek cells as they appear under the microscope (*Figure 6.5*). Label the **cytoplasm, nucleus,** and **plasma membrane.** Estimate the size of a typical cell. Record the cell size and magnification used.

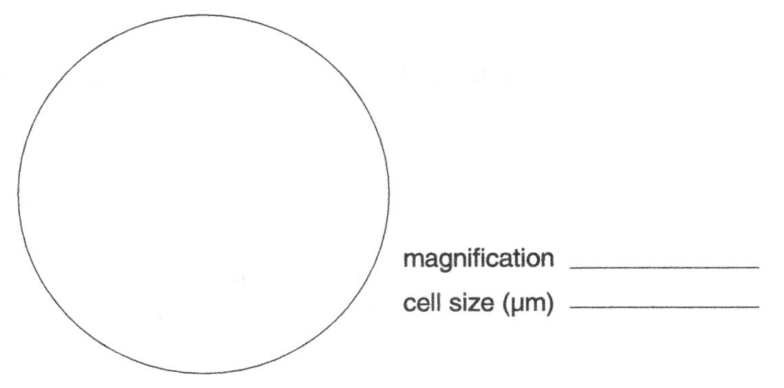

Figure 6.5 Drawing of the human cheek cell

EXERCISE 6.3 Animal cell organelles

With the help of special stains and the electron microscope, scientists have found many other structures within cells. These structures, called organelles, have specific functions necessary for the cell to survive.

1. Use your textbook and label the drawing of the animal cell (*Figure 6.10*).

2. View the three-dimensional model of the animal cell and identify each part. Note that the nucleus and mitochondria are each bounded by *two membranes*, which are referred to collectively as an **envelope.**

3. Use your textbook and identify the function of each animal cell organelle (*Table 6.2*).

B. Plant Cells

The leaves of growing tips of *Elodea* leaves are only a few cell layers thick making it possible to view individual cells (*Figure 6.6*).

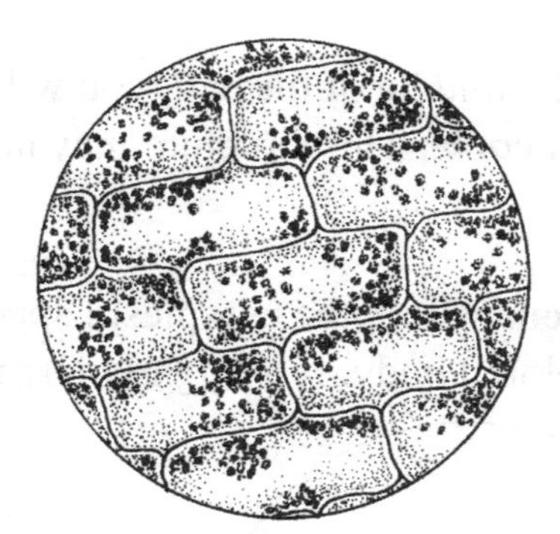

Figure 6.6 Elodea cell

EXERCISE 6.4 Prepare a wet mount of *Elodea* cells

1. Using forceps, remove a young leaf from the growing tip of an *Elodea* plant and prepare a wet mount.

2. Examine the leaf structure with low power. Then study the detail of several individual cells using high power.

3. Add a drop of safranin stain to make the cell wall more visible. Add the stain the same way you stained human cheek cells with methylene blue (*Figure 6.3*).

4. Carefully draw and label several *Elodea* cells in the field of view (*Figure 6.7*). Indicate where the plasma membrane is located in the cells.

You will notice many spherical green **chloroplasts** in the cytoplasm. These organelles function in photosynthesis and are necessary for plant life. The **cell wall** is found only in plants, monera, and fungi. When viewed through the microscope, it is a clear area outside of the cytoplasm. The **plasma membrane** is not visible because it is pressed tightly against the cell wall and because it is beyond the resolving power of the light microscope.

The light source may heat the cells and cause **cytoplasmic streaming**. This is evident by the movement of chloroplasts along the cell wall. Microfilaments are responsible for this intracellular motion. This motion is termed cytoplasmic streaming and serves two functions: it positions the chloroplasts toward light and distributes heat throughout the cell.

Toward the middle of the cell, you will find the large, water filled **central vacuole**. This structure may take up over half of the cell interior.

The **nucleus** within the cytoplasm appears as a clear or slightly amber-colored body. It is slightly larger than the chloroplasts.

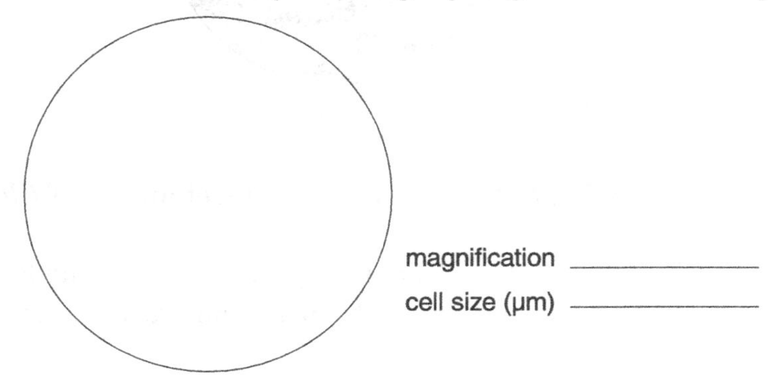

Figure 6.7 Drawing of Elodea cells

- Describe the three-dimensional shape of the *Elodea* cell.

- Describe the arrangement of the chloroplast, nucleus and vacuole within the cell.

EXERCISE 6.5 Onion bulb cells

1. Prepare a wet mount of onion epidermal cells (*Figure 6.8*).

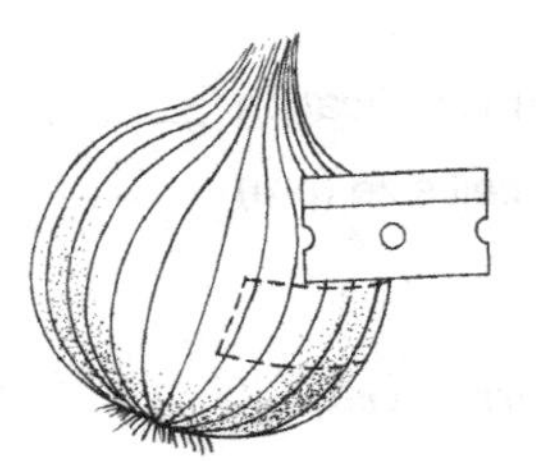

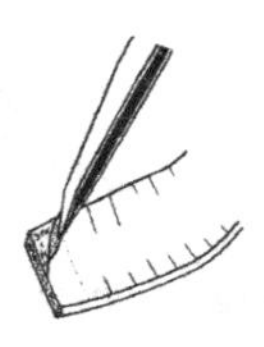

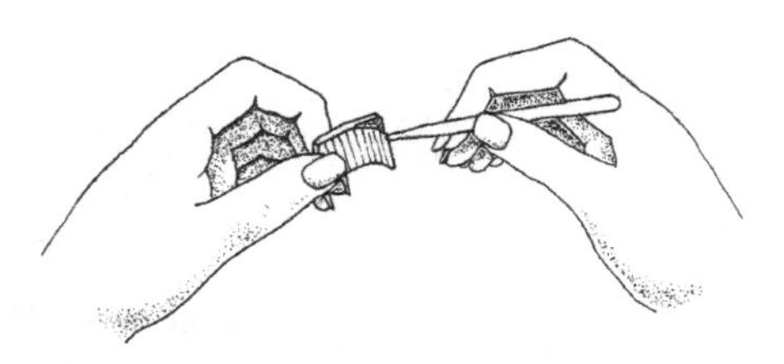

1. Using a razor blade, carefully cut a section from one bulb scale.

2. Using forceps, grasp the inner epidermis of the scale.

3. Remove the epidermis and prepare a wet mount.

Figure 6.8 Preparation of onion epidermis

2. Observe the wet mount under low power and then high power.

3. Stain the specimen with iodine as illustrated in *Figure 6.3*. The stain will increase the contrast and enable you to better view the nucleus, oil droplets, and cell wall.

4. The nucleus will be a large sphere within the cytoplasm. Examine the nucleus carefully and you will see several **nucleoli** inside the nucleus. Nucleoli are the areas within the nucleus where RNA (ribonucleic acid) is being synthesized. The rest of the nucleus is largely DNA (deoxyribonucleic acid), the genetic material.

5. Look for **oil droplets** in the form of granular material within the cytoplasm. The droplets are a form of stored food for the cell.

- What plant cell organelle is present in *Elodea* leaf cells that is absent in onion epidermal cells?
- What is the observable difference between the *Elodea* cell and onion epidermal cell?

6. Carefully draw and label several onion epidermal cells (*Figure 6.9*). Draw the cell size to scale.

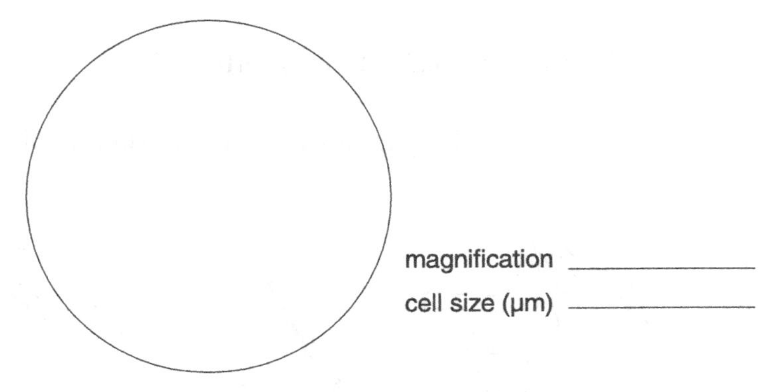

Figure 6.9 Drawing of onion epidermal cells

EXERCISE 6.6 Plant cell structure

The electron microscope has made it possible to observe great detail in plant cells.

1. Using your textbook and the plant cell model, label the drawing *Figure 6.11*.

2. Identify the function of each cell organelle (*Table 6.2*).

Structures found in both plant and animal cells	
plasma membrane	Golgi body
cytoplasm	mitochondria
nucleus: nucleoplasm	microtubules
nuclear envelope	ribosomes
nuclear pores	lysosome
DNA	vacuole
nucleolus	vacuolar membrane
endoplasmic reticulum (ER): rough ER (RER)	
smooth ER (SER)	
Structures unique to plant cells	**Structures unique to animal cells**
cell wall	centriole pair
large central vacuole	
chloroplast	
amyloplast	

Table 6.2 Comparison of plant and animal cell organelles

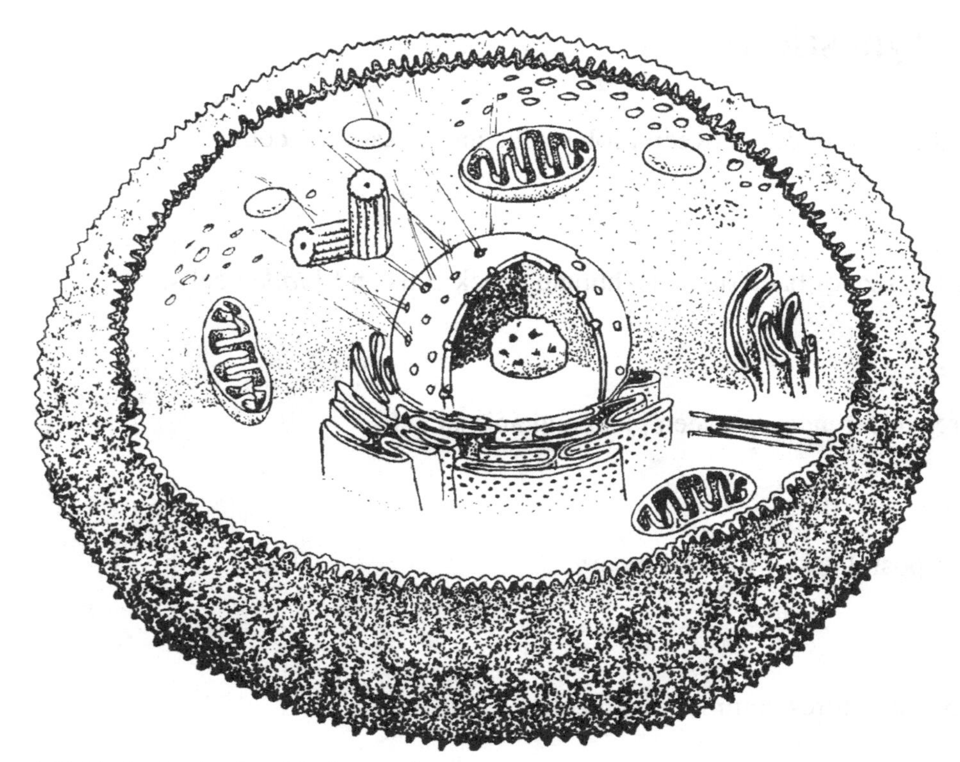

Figure 6.10 Typical animal cell (eukaryote)

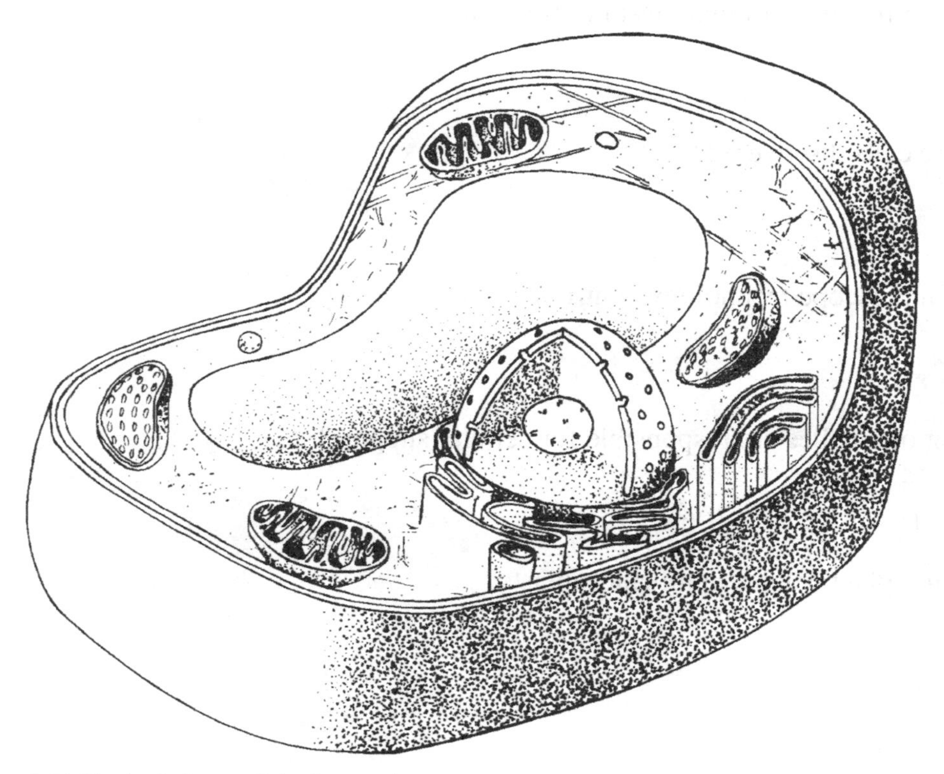

Figure 6.11 Typical plant cell (eukaryote)

Summary Questions

1. Describe the differences between prokaryotic and eukaryotic cells.

2. Compare the size of bacteria cells, human cheek cells and *Elodea* cells.

3. Name three differences between plant and animal cells.

4. State three postulates of the cell theory.

5. Name three structures common to all cells.

6. What are the functions of cytoplasmic streaming?

7. When were cells discovered?

8. How has microscope technology contributed to cell theory?

9. What plant organelles are responsible for cellular support?

10. Do *all* living plant cells contain chloroplasts?

APPENDIX 1 – Writing a Lab Report

(by Dwight Dimaculangan Ph.D.)

Objectives

After completing this unit you will:

- Know what the different components are in a scientific report
- Know how to communicate your results and conclusions generated from your experiments

Introduction

An important part of doing science is reporting the experiments that you did and what you found in order to disseminate the information and allow others to verify your results and conclusions. Although scientific writing contains less creativity and flair compared to other styles, scientists must be effective communicators with good writing skills.

To write an effective scientific report, you must present the question you addressed, how you intended to answer it, the results you obtained, and the conclusions you made, in a straightforward, logical, clear and orderly way. Scientific reports generally follow a structured format that has the following distinctive elements: Title, Introduction, Materials and Methods, Results, Discussion, and References (or Literature Cited).

For this class you will focus on writing the main parts of a report, although you will probably have shorter sections than a report you would submit to a scientific journal. Working in your small group, use the following exercise with one of the experiments that you conducted to help you learn how to write a scientific report.

EXERCISE:

1) The first task is to think of an appropriate **TITLE** for the report. Although you should make the title as brief as possible, it should be descriptive and informative enough so that someone reading your title will have a clear idea of the kind of work that is found in the report. Other information such as the organism that was studied, the particular system that was tested and the variable(s) that you manipulated should be included. Now, have each person in your group (working independently) write a possible title.

____

____

When everyone has finished, use the following questions to help critique each of the titles and decide which one is the best one. You may find that you need to fuse parts from several until you find one that is acceptable to all.

a) Can you tell from the title what experiment(s) was done?
b) Is the variable that you tested apparent?
c) Is it clear what was measured?
d) Do you know what organism was involved in the experiment? (NOTE: Scientists refer to organisms by their scientific name, which is composed of the genus and species. Where can you find this information?)

2) The next part to write is the **INTRODUCTION**. This section contains a statement of the question you addressed with your experiment and an explanation of why it was important to conduct the investigation. The introduction also contains background information about the organism and the system you are using, which helps to put the experiment into context and relate its significance.

If this were a scientific report you were going to submit for publication, you would need to do an extensive literature search to find the most current information about the organism you used, the type of experiment you did, and similar work that helped you form the working hypothesis that you addressed. However, because of the time constraints of this course, you should write an abbreviated introduction.

Have each person in the group write down at least three pieces of information that should be included in the introduction. Then, compare lists and work together as a group to write an introduction.

___

___

___

___

___

___

___

___

___

___

___

___

___

For this report the introduction only has to be a couple of paragraphs, but be sure you have addressed all of the questions below:

a) Is it clear what organism was used in the study and what it is about the organism that was of interest to study?
b) Is the question you tested clearly stated?
c) Is the working hypothesis that was used to design the experiment described? What about the null hypothesis and any alternate hypotheses?

3) Now let's address the **METHODS AND MATERIALS**. In this section you should give a thorough description of your experimental design, the procedures that you used, and the materials that you used for the experiment. It should supply enough information to allow others to repeat the experiment and get similar results. Think of this as a recipe in a cookbook where the writer tries to include as much information as possible including how much of each ingredient, where the ingredients were obtained, and a description of each step of the protocol.

However, unlike a cookbook where the ingredients are in a simple list and the directions are shown as series of numbered steps, the methods and materials section of a scientific report should be written in a past-tense narrative (i.e. you should describe what you did instead of telling the reader what to do).

Once again, work together to write the materials and methods and then use the questions below to evaluate your writing.

Be sure that the following questions are addressed in your materials and methods section:

a) Is it clear how you conducted the investigation? Be as specific and detailed as possible. Could anyone reading it repeat the experiment exactly as you have?
b) Did you describe what you measured and how you measured it?
c) Did you mention the type of organism(s) you used? What about how many organisms (sample size) and under what conditions?
d) Are all of the materials used in the study described, as well as how much of each and where you obtained them?
e) Did you describe the equipment that was used and how you used it in the study?
f) Did you describe the kind of data did you collected and how you analyzed your data?

4) The most important part of the report is the **RESULTS** section. This is the section where you present your data in tables and figures in a logical, organized way, as well as report the results of the statistical tests you used to analyze your data. HOWEVER, you should not interpret your results or state your opinion about them in this section. That type of analysis will be done in the Discussion section of the report.

   Although the data may be organized and shown in tables and graphs, it is not a substitute for a narrative description of your results. In other words you must describe what you found in sentences and make references to the data tables, figures, and the outcomes of the statistical tests throughout your presentation of the results.

   Start by having everyone in the group make an outline of how you will organize the data that will be presented. Then, compare outlines and write the results as a group.

Be sure you address the following questions in the results section of your report.

a) Are the results presented in a narrative form that refers to the tables and graphs?
b) Is it clear what experiment(s) was being done to obtain each of the results and what the null hypothesis being tested is for each statistical test?
c) Are the tables and graphs clearly marked with titles and legends?

5) Although the **DISCUSSION** is the last section that you need to write for your lab report, it is just as important as the others, because this is where you interpret and discuss the significance of your results. You should comment on whether or not the results support your working hypothesis. Normally you would also discuss how your results relate with experiments that were done by others, but for this assignment you are only expected to write a shortened version of this section.

   Have each person in the group write down at least three things that should be included in the discussion. Then, compare lists and work together as a group to write the discussion. For this report it only has to be a couple of paragraphs, but be sure you have addressed all of the questions below.

Be sure the following questions are addressed in your discussion section.

a) Did you indicate whether or not your results supported your working hypothesis? If not, what does that mean about your hypothesis? Is the hypothesis completely wrong or can it just be modified?
b) Is there even enough data to answer the questions in (a)?
c) If you did more than one experiment, were the results consistent with each other?
d) What problems did you encounter and how would you change your experiment to prevent the problems in future experiments?

6.) Now that you have a start on the scientific report, go back and edit your paper. Go to the library and look up some background information on your organism and the system you are using for your study, including the genus and species name of the organism. Then incorporate this information into the report.

APPENDIX 2 – Using the Microscope

(by Dwight Dimaculangan Ph.D.)

Objectives

After completing this unit you will be able to:

- Identify the parts of a compound microscope
- Use a light microscope with different objective lenses

Introduction

Some of the observations that you will make in this course will require the use of microscopes. These are delicate instruments, which if used correctly, will provide a powerful means to see microscopic objects. A very common type of microscope, the compound light microscope, can magnify objects over 1,000 times using two lenses placed in a tube at calculated intervals. Before you use the microscope, let's review its various parts.

EXERCISE:

1. Identify the Parts of the Microscope
Obtain a microscope from your instructor and place it on the table in front of you so that you can look at its profile. Compare it to the figure on the next page. Notice at the top of the microscope there are two removable tubes called the oculars (or eye pieces). Each ocular contains several lenses and fits into the head of the microscope. At the other end of the head is a disk-shaped turntable called the nosepiece, in which are inserted 3 or 4 small tubes with lenses called the objective lenses. The shortest objective has the lowest power and has a magnification of 4X. The intermediate sized objectives have magnifying power of 10X, and the highest-powered objective is 40X. The number is engraved on the side of the objective housing.

The adjustment knobs are located on the side of the body of the microscope and are used to bring the specimen into the plane of focus. The large knob is called the course adjustment, and the small knob is called the fine adjustment. The curved part of the frame is referred to as the arm. Attached to the arm just below the objective lens is a flat surface called the stage. The stage has a hole in the center through which light passes from a source below the stage to the specimen and up through the microscope lenses to your eyes. The slide is held to the stage by a spring-loaded mechanical stage. Below the stage there is a movable substage condenser with a built-in iris diaphragm. These devices are used to focus the light precisely on the object being viewed.

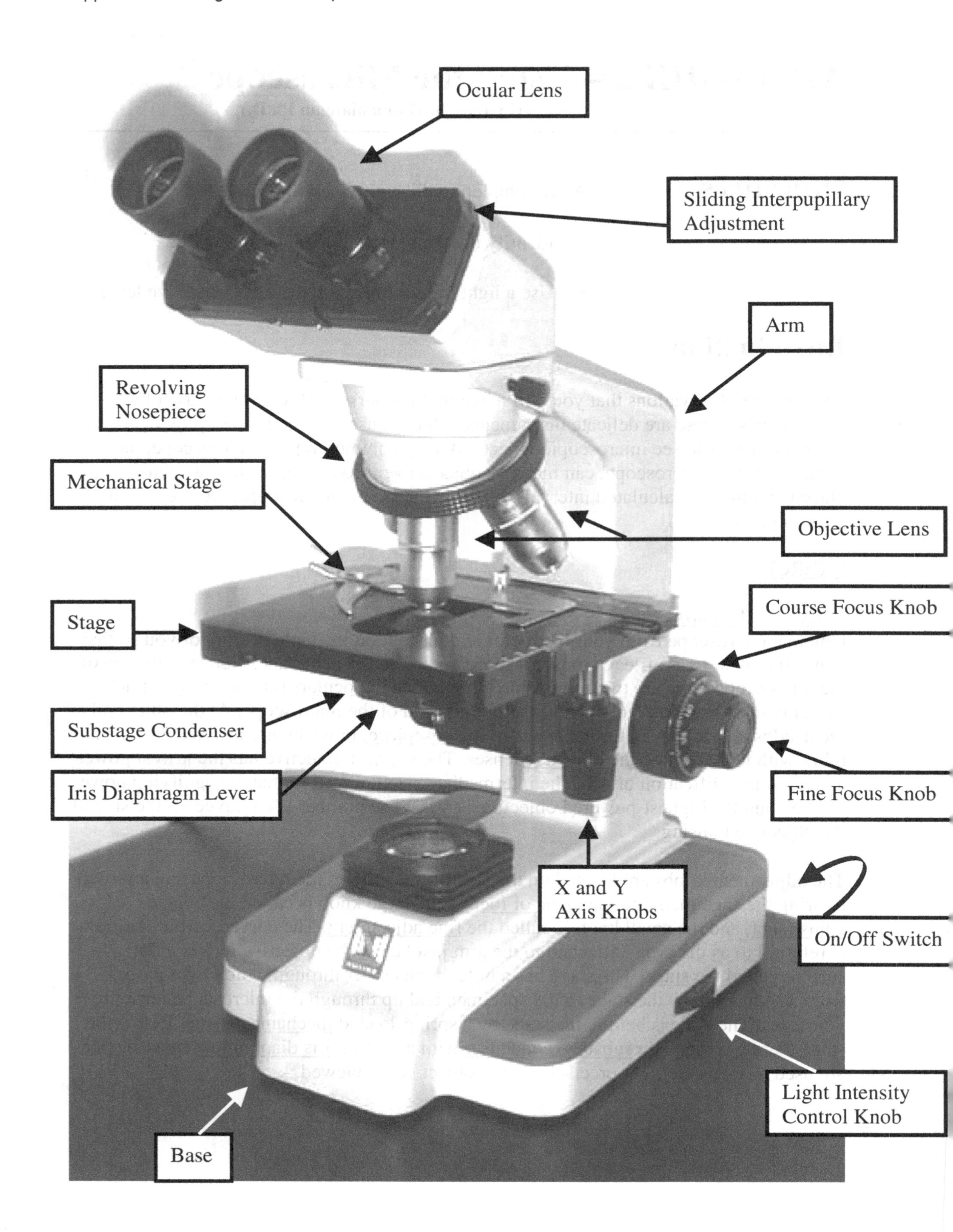
Ocular Lens
Sliding Interpupillary Adjustment
Arm
Revolving Nosepiece
Mechanical Stage
Objective Lens
Stage
Course Focus Knob
Substage Condenser
Iris Diaphragm Lever
Fine Focus Knob
X and Y Axis Knobs
On/Off Switch
Light Intensity Control Knob
Base

2. Cleaning:

A microscope is only as good as the condition of its lenses. They must be kept free of dirt, dust, oil, lint and eye make-up. **Do not use cloth or ordinary paper tissue of any kind to clean the lenses as they will scratch the soft glass used in the manufacture of microscope lenses. The only acceptable method that may be used to clean the lenses is by wiping gently with a dry piece of clean lens paper.** You should clean the microscope lenses before and after each time you use the microscope.

3. Magnification:

The microscope contains a series of lenses arranged to produce an image on the retina of your eye. Each lens magnifies the specimen independently. In order to determine the magnification of a combination of lenses, multiply the power of the objective lens by the power of the ocular lens. Most ocular lenses are 10X. The apparent size and position of the specimen under the microscope is called the virtual image or field of view. It appears to be about 10 inches away from your eye. The depth of focus is the thickness of the specimen that appears in focus at any one time. As you use lenses of higher magnification the depth of focus will decrease. This is why you have to adjust the focus more frequently for higher power lenses than for lower power lenses.

4. Operation:

Follow the steps listed below to produce the best microscopic image of high resolution.

a) Place the microscope on the bench in front of you and check to make sure the power button is turned off.
b) Before plugging in the microscope, adjust the light intensity control knob to the minimum position. This should be done prior to each time the light is turned on or off (This will extend the bulb life). Then plug the microscope in, turn the power on, and adjust the intensity of the light to match the requirements of the objective and specimen slide.
c) Adjust the distance between the ocular lenses to fit your eyes by looking through the microscope and moving the interpupillary adjustment. When a full field of view is observed through both tubes, and the images blend into one, the interpupillary distance is correct for your eyes. Check the interpupillary scale and note the index reading for future reference, in case other users change the adjustment.
d) Adjust the diopter scales, located at each ocular, to the same numerical value as indicated on the interpupillary scale. This must be done in order to maintain parfocality of the objective lenses.
e) Position the 4x objective lens into the optical path, making sure that the lens in properly indexed in its click-stop position.
f) Place a specimen slide on top of the stage surface and hold it in place swining the moveable finger on the mechanical stage outward. Then place the slide against the fixed side of the holder, and slowly release the moveable finger until it makes contact with the specimen slide.

g) Using the X and Y-axis knobs, position the specimen slide so that the object to be viewed is in the exact center of the annulus. At this point there should be a circle of light illuminating the specimen.
h) Now look through the microscope and start rotating the course focus knob until the specimen comes into focus, and adjust the fine focus controls until the specimen in is in sharp focus.
i) Adjust the diopter for differences in eyesight between your eyes. To do this close your left eye and use your right eye to peer into the right ocular. Adjust the sharpness of the image using the fine focus controls. Then, close your right eye and use your left eye to peer into the left ocular. This time adjust the sharpness of the image by turning the diopter adjustment located at the left ocular.
j) Adjust the aperture (opening) of the iris diaphragm.
Note: The iris diaphragm should not be used to control the brightness of illumination. The iris diaphragms are designed to help achieve high resolution of the specimen and to provide contrast in the image. Smaller apertures will deliver higher contrast to the image. However, closing the aperture too much will reduce the resolution. Experimentation is the best method of determining the correct opening of the diaphragm.

5. Changing magnification:
   a) Rotate the revolving nosepiece until the 10X objective is in the optical path. Since this microscope is parfocal, it allows changes from one objective to another with only a slight adjustment of the fine focus controls.
   b) When changing to the 40X objective lens, care must be exercised in order to prevent damaging the front lens element and the specimen slide.

6. Storing the microscope:
   When you are finished using the microscope, turn the light intensity control knob all the way down, switch the power button to the off position, and clean the objective lenses with lens paper. Then, the rotate the nosepiece so that the 4X objective is in the optical path, wrap the power cord around the arm of the microscope base and place the dust cover on the microscope.

7. Observing hair:
   a) Place a drop of water in the middle of a slide.
   b) Place a piece of your hair in the drop of water and put a coverslip on top. Try not to get any bubbles under the coverslip.
   c) Observe the hair with the 10X objective first and then the 40X objective.
   d) Record your observations below using the circles for your drawings.

[Certain parts of this appendix were adopted from the National Optical & Scientific Instruments Inc. instructions for 160 series compound biological microscropes]

Specimen:____________________

Magnification:_________________

Notes:_______________________

____

Specimen:____________________

Magnification:_________________

Notes:_______________________

____

Specimen:____________________

Magnification:_________________

Notes:_______________________

____

Specimen:____________________

Magnification:_________________

Notes:_______________________

____

APPENDIX 3 - Redesigning an Experiment

Disinfectant Lab II By Jennifer Wearly – M.S.

Introduction

When we are doing science, it is important for our results to be reliable and scientifically sound. We want **consistent** materials and methods, as well as data that are able to be tested **statistically** for significance. **Controls** are also essential to a good experiment, in order to assure that the results are not clouded by multiple variables.

1.) In the first run of the disinfectant experiment, there were many variables that were not controlled for. List three such factors that would have potentially made the results unreliable:

-
-
-

Researchers often redesign experiments if they realize there might be a better way to test their hypothesis and produce more reliable results.

Today, we will redesign our disinfectant experiment in a more controlled manner. In the first disinfectant experiment, recall that you chose various surfaces to swab as your source of bacteria. You then **inoculated** a nutrient media (**agar**) plate with your bacterial sample and tested the effectiveness of a disinfectant. When applied to the agar, the bacteria and other microbes divided and eventually formed colonies that were visible to the naked eye. Keep in mind that these colonies that you saw were actually thousands or even millions of individual bacterial cells.

On your agar plates, how many different-looking colonies did you see? Different species of bacteria (as well as fungi) have characteristically different colonies. Different colors, different textures, different shapes; if a colony looks different than the one growing next to it, they are most likely a different species!

2.) Do you think that disinfectants may be effective against certain types of bacteria, and not against others? How could you make your test of disinfectant effectiveness more reliable?

It is possible to obtain a *single type* of bacterium and apply it to an agar plate. Left alone and incubated, the plate will become covered with an even "lawn" of bacterial growth (the surface of the agar will appear to be coated with a cloudy film). We can test bacterial response to specific disinfectants by applying disinfectant-soaked discs to the surface of the agar after the agar has been **inoculated** with bacteria. After the bacteria are incubated, a **zone of inhibition** can be seen around the disc if the disinfectant was effective against the bacteria. This "zone of clearance" shows that the bacteria were unable to grow or killed because of the chemical. Everywhere else on the agar, the film of bacterial growth *should* be visible. See Figure One.

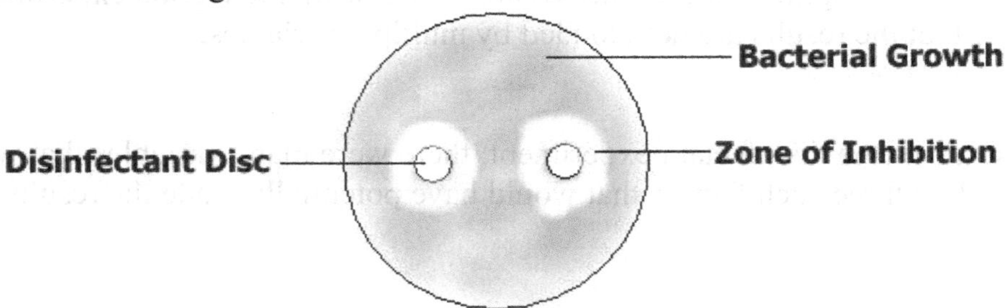

Figure 1. Zones of inhibition on an agar dish after incubation.

3.) By using this method, what are some of the things that we now "control for", that we couldn't previously?

-
-
-

Another benefit to this experimental design is that it yields *measurable* results! The zones of inhibition can actually be measured with a ruler or caliper, which you will do after your agar dishes have been incubated.

Procedure

1.) Work with the person sitting next to you. Obtain an agar dish that has already been inoculated with a known strain of bacteria. The dish should have a line drawn down the middle. Label one side of the side of the dish "C" for "Control", and the other side "E" for "Experimental".

2.) With a pair of sterile forceps, dip one paper disc into your disinfectant. Tap off excess liquid, and apply it to the

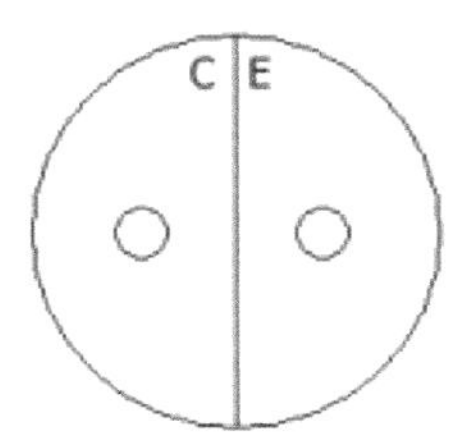

"Experimental" side of the agar dish by tapping down lightly. Don't pierce the surface of the agar! (See figure to the right.)

3.) On the "Control" side of the dish, you will follow the same procedure, except you will be using distilled water rather than disinfectant on your two discs.

4.) Make sure your dishes are labeled around the edge with your group number and section number, and give them to your TA to be put in the incubator.

4.) Based on your previous knowledge and experience, which disinfectant do you hypothesize will be the most effective? Be sure to support your hypothesis with some explanation.

Results

Table 1. Experimental Results

Group	Disinfectant	Zone of Inhibition-Experimental (mm)	Zone of Inhibition-Control (mm)
1			
1			
2			
2			
3			
3			
4			
4			
5			
5			
6			
6			

Review Questions

1.) Why did we use a control disc that had only been soaked in water?

2.) If the size of the zone of inhibition around a disc is related to the effectiveness of the disinfectant, what would a *larger* zone of inhibition suggest?

3.) What improvements could you make to this experiment? What are some things that still weren't controlled for?